D0486689

English

The 11+ 10-Minute Tests

For GL & other test providers

Book 1

Ages

10-11

Practise • Prepare • Pass

Everything your child needs for 11+ success

How to use this book

This book is made up of 10-minute tests and puzzle pages.
There are answers and detailed explanations in the pull-out section at the back of the book.

10-Minute Tests

*   There are 33 tests in this book, consisting of 17 comprehension tests worth 9 marks each, and 16 proofreading tests worth 18 marks each. Each test is a bite-sized version of a full-length 11+ test, focusing on either the comprehension part or the proofreading part of the test.

*   Each test is designed to cover a good range of the question styles and topics that your child could come across in their 11+ test, at the same difficulty level.

*   Your child should aim to score at least 8 out of 9 in each comprehension test and 16 out of 18 in each proofreading test. If they score less than this, use their results to work out the areas they need more practice on.

*   If your child hasn't managed to finish the test in time, they need to work on increasing their speed, whereas if they have made a lot of mistakes, they need to work more carefully.

*   Keep track of your child's scores using the progress chart on the inside back cover of the book.

Puzzle Pages

*   There are 10 puzzle pages in this book, which are a great break from test-style questions. They encourage children to practise the same skills that they will need in the test, but in a fun way.

Published by CGP

Editors:
Joanna Daniels, Rachel Grocott, Heather McClelland

With thanks to Holly Poynton and Alison Griffin for the proofreading.
With thanks to Jan Greenway for the copyright research.

ISBN: 978 1 78294 255 9
Printed by Elanders Ltd, Newcastle upon Tyne
Clipart from Corel®

Based on the classic CGP style created by Richard Parsons.

Text, design, layout and original illustrations © Coordination Group Publications Ltd. (CGP) 2015
All rights reserved.

Photocopying this book is not permitted. Extra copies are available from CGP with next day delivery.
0800 1712 712 • www.cgpbooks.co.uk

Contents

Test 1: Comprehension

You have **10 minutes** to do this test. Work as quickly and accurately as you can.

Read this passage carefully and answer the questions that follow.

The Eiffel Tower

The Eiffel Tower characterises the Paris skyline, and it is one of the world's most famous monuments, drawing over 7 million visitors every year. Like a giraffe stretching for the leaves from the highest trees, the Eiffel Tower looms above France's capital.

5 The Eiffel Tower was designed as an entry for the World's Fair — a celebration held in Paris between May and October, 1889. Before it was built, however, its design was condemned by several French artists. They believed that a metal structure the size of the Eiffel Tower would detract significantly from the traditional beauty of Paris's other famous monuments, such as the cathedral of Notre Dame and the
10 Arc de Triomphe.

However, the engineer in charge of the project, Gustave Eiffel, was confident that people would come to admire his project. Topping 300 metres in height, the Eiffel Tower was the tallest man-made structure in the world — a title it would keep until the Chrysler Building skyscraper was completed in 1930.

15 The tower opened to the public on the 6th May, and, as Eiffel had predicted, the exhibition was a hit. Over 28 million visitors came to the World's Fair, and passed under the legs of this giant, with 1,896,987 visitors ascending the tower itself. Since then, over 250 million people have admired the view of Paris from the tower's balconies — ascending either by the lifts or by climbing its many steps.

20 The Eiffel Tower had permission to stay in place for twenty years. However, Paris officials decided that the tower served as an effective communications tower, especially for sending wireless telegraph signals. In 1910, the tower was granted a reprieve, and since then has become an iconic feature of both Paris and France.

2

Answer these questions about the text. You can refer back to the text if you need to.

1. Explain what is meant by "The Eiffel Tower characterises the Paris skyline" (line 1).

It meant by The Eiffel Tower characterises Paris skyline is making the sky more beautiful and better to look at.

2. Find a phrase from the text that contains a simile.

The phrase from the text that contains a simile is "Like a giraffe stretching for the leaves"

3. Give another word or phrase that means the same as "condemned" (line 7) as it is used in the text.

_____

4. Why were some people not in favour of the Eiffel Tower?
   Tick the box next to the correct answer.

   A Because it would obstruct people's view of the Paris skyline ☐

   B Because it would be an eyesore ☐

   C Because it would steal the show at the World's Fair ☐

   D Because it would make other monuments less attractive ☑

5. "However, the engineer in charge of the project, Gustave Eiffel, was confident that people would come to admire his project." (Lines 11-12). Which word in this sentence is an adjective? Tick the box next to the correct answer.

   A However ☐

   B confident ☑

   C project ☐

   D admire ☐

TURN OVER ➡

6. What happened when the tower opened to the public?
Tick the box next to the correct answer.

A	Gustave was surprised to see so many visitors.	☐
B	Gustave arranged for the tower to remain in the city for longer.	☐
C	Gustave's prediction about its success was confirmed.	☑
D	Gustave's detractors were proved right.	☐

7. "the legs of this giant" (line 17). What is this phrase an example of?
Tick the box next to the correct answer.

A	A metaphor	☐
B	Irony	☐
C	Hyperbole	☐
D	A contradiction	☑

8. What secondary purpose did the tower have?

_____

_____

9. In your own words, what happened to the tower in 1910?

In 1910 the Eiffel Tower became the new ~~famit~~ and most famous
tower in Paris/France.

END OF TEST

5. / 9

4

You have **10 minutes** to do this test. Work as quickly and accurately as you can.

> This passage contains some spelling mistakes.
> Write the passage out again with the correct spellings.

1. To help me remeber Ian's birthday, I put a note on my calender in big, bold letters.
    I forgot about it last year, and it was very embarassing. He looked so disapointed
    when I next saw him, and I felt terrable.

    _____

    _____

    _____

    _____

> This passage has some punctuation mistakes.
> Write the passage out again with the correct punctuation.

2. the waiter looked at Fred. Hell have a fruit salad," said his sister. Fred scowled, and
    looked longingly at a piece of cake but he didn't say anything

    _____

    _____

    _____

    _____

TURN OVER ➡

For each numbered line, choose the word, or group of words, which completes the passage correctly. The passage needs to make sense and be written in correct English. Circle the correct letter.

3. Chocolate is possibly the most popular snack **what who that where when**
   A B C D E

4. is available in our shops, **since so despite consequently but** most people
   A B C D E

5. **don't doesn't does not didn't hadn't** know how it's made. First of all, the
   A B C D E

6. cocoa beans are harvested, fermented and then **their there those they're these**
   A B C D E

7. dried in the sun. Next, the beans **is are were will be have been** roasted.
   A B C D E

8. A further stage, known **by of to for as** 'cracking and winnowing', separates
   A B C D E

   cocoa nibs from their shells. After this, the nibs are ground into a thick paste. The

9. flavour of this paste is then improved, and **its her their his it's** texture
   A B C D E

10. is enhanced **while with when and so** a process called 'conching'. The
    A B C D E

    chocolate is then tempered to give it a glossy look before it is finally cooled.

END OF TEST

/ 18

You have **10 minutes** to do this test. Work as quickly and accurately as you can.

Read this passage carefully and answer the questions that follow.

Adapted from 'Story of the Bandbox'

Up to the age of sixteen, at a private school and afterwards at one of those great institutions for which England is justly famous, Mr. Harry Hartley had received the ordinary education of a gentleman. At that period he manifested a remarkable distaste for study; and his only surviving parent being both weak and ignorant, he
5 was permitted thenceforward to spend his time in the attainment of petty and purely elegant accomplishments. Two years later, he was left an orphan and almost a beggar. For all active and industrious pursuits, Harry was unfitted alike by nature and training. He could sing romantic ditties, and accompany himself with discretion on the piano; he was a graceful although a timid cavalier*; he had a pronounced
10 taste for chess; and nature had sent him into the world with one of the most engaging exteriors that can well be fancied. Blond and pink, with dove's eyes and a gentle smile, he had an air of agreeable tenderness and melancholy and the most submissive and caressing manners. But when all is said, he was not the man to lead armaments of war or direct the councils of a State.
15 A fortunate chance and some influence obtained for Harry, at the time of his bereavement, the position of private secretary to Major-General Sir Thomas Vandeleur, C.B. Sir Thomas was a man of sixty, loud-spoken, boisterous, and domineering. For some reason, some service the nature of which had been often whispered and repeatedly denied, the Rajah of Kashgar had presented this officer
20 with the sixth known diamond of the world. The gift transformed General Vandeleur from a poor into a wealthy man, from an obscure and unpopular soldier into one of the lions of London society.

Robert Louis Stevenson

* cavalier — *horseman*

TURN OVER ➡

7

Answer these questions about the text. You can refer back to the text if you need to.

1. What is meant by the term "institutions" in line 2?
    Tick the box next to the correct answer.

    A   Private schools   ☐

    B   Banks   ☐

    C   Universities   ☐

    D   Orphanages   ☐

2. Why was Harry able to spend his time on leisure pursuits?

    _____

    _____

3. "For all active and industrious pursuits, Harry was unfitted alike by nature
    and training." (Lines 7-8). What does this tell you about Harry?

    _____

4. "Blond and pink, with **dove's eyes** and a gentle smile" (lines 11-12). What is
    the phrase in bold an example of? Tick the box next to the correct answer.

    A   Onomatopoeia   ☐

    B   A paraphrase   ☐

    C   Personification   ☐

    D   A metaphor   ☐

5. Which of the words below is closest in meaning to the word "submissive" (line 13)?
    Tick the box next to the correct answer.

    A   Compliant   ☐

    B   Caring   ☐

    C   Calming   ☐

    D   Reflective   ☐

6. Why did Harry become Sir Thomas's private secretary?
    Tick the box next to the correct answer.

    A   On account of his handsome appearance   ☐

    B   Through a stroke of luck and his connections   ☐

    C   Due to his unsuitability for leadership roles   ☐

    D   Because Sir Thomas empathised with Harry's situation   ☐

7. Give another word or phrase that means the same as
    "boisterous" (line 17) as it is used in the text.

    _____

8. Describe how Sir Thomas's personality traits compare to Harry's.

    _____

    _____

9. The reason why the Rajah of Kashgar gave Sir Thomas a diamond is a secret.
    Which information in the text tells you this?

    _____

    _____

END OF TEST

/ 9

Good **grammar** and **logic** skills are needed for this puzzle page. Thinking caps on!

Inspector English's Investigation

Inspector English is interrogating Mr Gobbledygook, but he needs your help. Mr Gobbledygook's answers contain grammar errors, and Inspector English can't understand what he's saying. Rewrite Mr Gobbledygook's answers on the dotted lines and correct his mistakes.

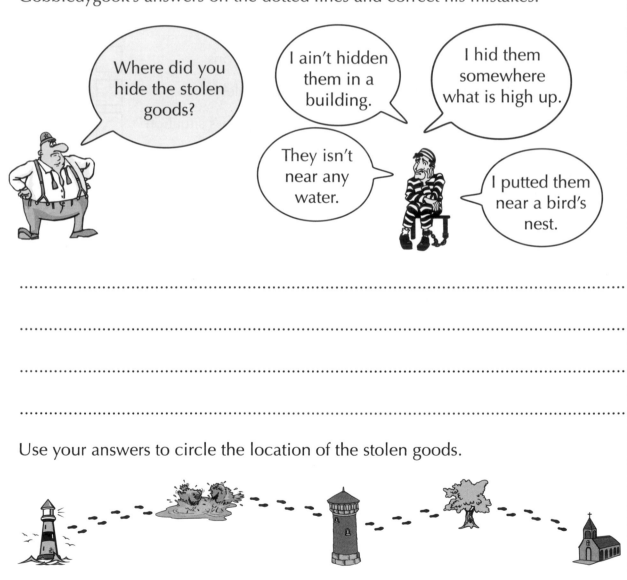

Where did you hide the stolen goods?

I ain't hidden them in a building.

I hid them somewhere what is high up.

They isn't near any water.

I putted them near a bird's nest.

Use your answers to circle the location of the stolen goods.

You have **10 minutes** to do this test. Work as quickly and accurately as you can.

For each numbered line, choose the word which completes the passage correctly. The passage needs to make sense and be written in correct English. Circle the correct letter.

1. Lianne, my friend, **who whose which whom who's** advice I value, told me
    A   B   C   D   E

2. I should **of off have not be** mentioned my problem sooner. She reminded
    A   B   C   D   E

3. me that she **had been has been is being have been was being** at home until
    A   B   C   D   E

4. 11 o'clock that morning. I **should ought could must shall** to have called.
    A   B   C   D   E

This passage contains some spelling mistakes.
Write the passage out again with the correct spellings.

5. Kerry acheived an excellent mark in her spelling test. She found the begining of the test challengeing, but since she had practiced the words beforehand, she remained confidant that she would be succesful.

_____

_____

_____

_____

TURN OVER ➡

Test 4

This passage contains some punctuation mistakes. Each numbered line has either one mistake or no mistake. For each line, work out which group of words contains a mistake, and circle the correct letter. Circle N if there is no mistake.

6. There's a heated discussion going on in the staffroom about the teachers Christmas

   A   B   C   D   N

7. party. Mr Hitchen, whos Scottish, wants to entertain the others with his bagpipes,

   A   B   C   D   N

8. but Mrs Reid objects: she thinks a disco would be better. And with regard to the

   A   B   C   D   N

9. food everyone has decided that a traditional turkey dinner is the best option.

   A   B   C   D   N

10. I'm not eating sprouts though," Miss Isherwood announced at the top of her voice.

   A   B   C   D   N

11. Miss Dandy looked surprised, "Its Christmas. You've got to eat sprouts!" she said.

   A   B   C   D   N

12. "Never mind the sprouts," interrupted Mr Edwards, "we don't have a venue!"

   A   B   C   D   N

13. "Oh well," sighed Mrs Preston, "we could always have it in the school canteen"

   A   B   C   D   N

END OF TEST

/ 18

You have **10 minutes** to do this test. Work as quickly and accurately as you can.

Read this passage carefully and answer the questions that follow.

The Lonely House

I know some lonely houses off the road
A robber 'd like the look of, —
Wooden barred,
And windows hanging low,
5   Inviting to
A portico*,
Where two could creep:
One hand the tools,
The other peep
10 To make sure all's asleep.
Old-fashioned eyes,
Not easy to surprise!

How orderly the kitchen 'd look by night,
With just a clock, —
15 But they could gag the tick,
And mice won't bark;
And so the walls don't tell,
None will.

A pair of spectacles ajar just stir —
20 An almanac's* aware.
Was it the mat winked,
Or a nervous star?
The moon slides down the stair
To see who's there.

25 There's plunder, — where?
Tankard, or spoon,
Earring, or stone,
A watch, some ancient brooch
To match the grandmamma,
30 Staid* sleeping there.

Day rattles, too,
Stealth's slow;
The sun has got as far
As the third sycamore.
35 Screams chanticleer*,
"Who's there?"
And echoes, trains away,
Sneer — "Where?"
While the old couple, just astir,
40 Fancy the sunrise left the door ajar!

Emily Dickinson

* portico — *porch*
* almanac — *a type of calendar*
* staid — *respectable*
* chanticleer — *cockerel*

TURN OVER ➡

             Test 5

Answer these questions about the text. You can refer back to the text if you need to.

1. Give one reason why this house attracts the burglars.

   _____

   _____

2. "Old-fashioned eyes" (line 11).
   What does this line suggest about the occupants of the house?

   _____

3. Which of the words below is closest in meaning to the word "gag" (line 15) as it
   is used in the text? Tick the box next to the correct answer.

   A   Break   ☐

   B   Restrain   ☐

   C   Mimic   ☐

   D   Silence   ☐

4. What atmosphere do you think the author is trying to create in lines 19-24?

   _____

5. "a nervous star" (line 22). What is this phrase an example of?
   Tick the box next to the correct answer.

   A   Alliteration   ☐

   B   Rhyme   ☐

   C   Personification   ☐

   D   Characterisation   ☐

6. What do the tankard, the spoon, the brooch and the stone have in common?
    Tick the box next to the correct answer.

    A   They are the grandfather's possessions. ☐

    B   They are the items which the thieves are looking for. ☐

    C   They are very old. ☐

    D   They are valuable items. ☐

7. Give another word or phrase that means the same as
    "stealth" (line 32) as it is used in the text.

    _____

8. "The sun has got as far / As the third sycamore." (Lines 33-34).
    Explain what these lines mean in your own words.

    _____

    _____

9. What is the final clue that the house has been burgled?
    Tick the box next to the correct answer.

    A   The occupants are awoken. ☐

    B   A cockerel spies the intruders. ☐

    C   The door has been left open. ☐

    D   The sun shines on an empty house. ☐

END OF TEST

/ 9

You have **10 minutes** to do this test. Work as quickly and accurately as you can.

Read this passage carefully and answer the questions that follow.

Alfred Wainwright

Alfred Wainwright has delighted, informed and inspired fellwalkers for decades with his guides to the Lake District fells*.

Born in Blackburn, Lancashire in 1907, Wainwright lived with his parents and three siblings. His father was a stonemason, but he was often unemployed. Despite
5 being academically gifted, Wainwright left school aged thirteen. Unlike other boys his age, he avoided having to work in the mills and was employed as an office worker for Blackburn council. He attended night school and gained qualifications which provided him with opportunities to advance.

Wainwright went to the Lake District for the very first time when he was 23. He
10 climbed a hill near lake Windermere and was astounded by the view of the fells, the trees and the lake below. What he saw was in stark contrast to the industrial town he lived in. This trip started his life-long passion for the Lake District. In 1941, he moved to the area and spent much of his spare time walking in the fells. He grew to know them intimately.

15 In 1952, he began writing the books for which he was most famous: his seven pictorial guides to the Lake District, which took 13 years to complete. He described them as his 'love letter' to the Lakeland fells. They give incredibly accurate and detailed information about 214 fells in the Lake District, including handwritten route descriptions and hand-drawn maps, diagrams and pictures. The fells in these
20 books are known as 'Wainwrights' and many walkers set themselves the challenge of ascending all of these fells over their lifetime.

Wainwright's favourite fell was Haystacks, and it was here that his ashes were scattered after his death in 1991.

*fells — *hills*

Answer the following questions about the text. You can refer back to the text if you need to.

16

1. Who is the target audience of Wainwright's books?
   Tick the box next to the correct answer.

   A   People born in Lancashire   ☐

   B   Rambling enthusiasts   ☐

   C   Tree fellers   ☐

   D   Council workers   ☐

2. Which word below best describes Wainwright's social background?
   Tick the box next to the correct answer.

   A   Destitute   ☐

   B   Privileged   ☐

   C   Humble   ☐

   D   Abusive   ☐

3. What does the text say about Wainwright's employment?
   Tick the box next to the correct answer.

   A   He began a career in the mills in 1920.   ☐

   B   Blackburn council hired him to work in their recruitment department.   ☐

   C   He refused to work alongside his peers in the mills.   ☐

   D   Evening classes supported his career development.   ☐

4. Which of the words below is closest in meaning to the word "stark" (line 11) as it
   is used in the text? Tick the box next to the correct answer.

   A   Complete   ☐

   B   True   ☐

   C   Bare   ☐

   D   Picturesque   ☐

TURN OVER ➡

5. What was the catalyst for Wainwright's enthusiasm for the Lake District?

   _____

6. Give another word or phrase that means the same as
   "intimately" (line 14) as it is used in the text.

   _____

7. Explain why Wainwright described his pictorial guides to the Lake District
   as his "'love letter' to the Lakeland fells" (line 17).

   _____

   _____

8. "They give incredibly accurate and detailed information about 214 fells in the
   Lake District" (lines 17-18). Which word in this sentence is an adverb?
   Tick the box next to the correct answer.

   A   accurate   ☐

   B   information   ☐

   C   about   ☐

   D   incredibly   ☐

9. When talking about the fells in Wainwright's guides, the text says "many walkers
   set themselves the challenge of ascending all of these fells over their lifetime"
   (lines 20-21). What does this tell us about the fells?

   _____

   _____

END OF TEST

/ 9

Puzzles 2

It's time for some puzzles that will test your knowledge of **homographs** and **punctuation**.

Word Connections

The word pairs below each have a word in common. Fill in the gaps to link the words on the left to the words on the right. The word in the middle should have a similar meaning to the word on the left **and** the word on the right. One has already been done for you.

Hint: the word in the middle might have two different pronunciations.

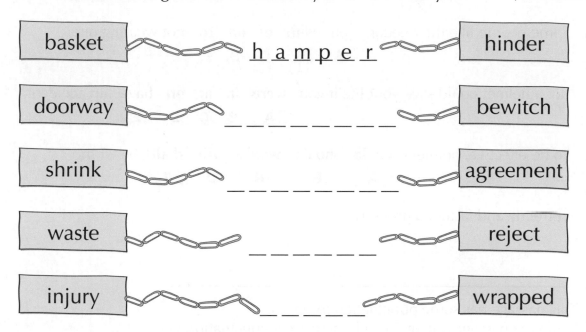

basket	h a m p e r	hinder
doorway	_ _ _ _ _ _ _	bewitch
shrink	_ _ _ _ _ _ _	agreement
waste	_ _ _ _ _ _	reject
injury	_ _ _ _ _	wrapped

Punctuation Pandemonium

Eric wrote down the statements below without using punctuation correctly. A police officer found these statements, and now Eric is in serious trouble. Help Eric out by punctuating each sentence correctly.

I love cooking my family and my cat.

I think it's time to eat Dad.

You have **10 minutes** to do this test. Work as quickly and accurately as you can.

For each numbered line, choose the word which completes the passage correctly. The passage needs to make sense and be written in correct English. Circle the correct letter.

1. It's a good idea to wear a helmet **after** **once** **following** **when** **where** cycling.
    A   B   C   D   E

2. Some people like the freedom **on** **with** **of** **off** **to** not wearing one,
    A   B   C   D   E

3. but a helmet could save your life if you **were** **in** **at** **on** **have** an accident.
    A   B   C   D   E

4. To be effective, helmets **could** **should** **would** **will** **shall** be worn
    A   B   C   D   E

correctly and fastened properly.

This passage has some punctuation mistakes.
Write the passage out again with the correct punctuation.

5. Look, there it is" said Ashleigh, pointing at the long grass You've found it," I shouted in excitement running over to where she was standing.

_____

_____

_____

This passage contains some spelling mistakes. Each numbered line has either one mistake or no mistake. For each line, work out which group of words contains a mistake, and circle the correct letter. Circle N if there is no mistake.

Dear Mum and Dad,

6. I'm having a brillient time on my school trip. The youth hostel we're staying in is

    A   B   C   D   N

7. adjacent to the lake, so there are beutiful views of the islands. We paddled to one

    A   B   C   D   N

8. of them and had a picnic when we went caneoing yesterday. Jack was the only

    A   B   C   D   N

9. person to capsize — it was hilarious. He resurfaced covered in slimy pondweed.

    A   B   C   D   N

10. Tomorrow, we're going to the pencil musuem which I'm very excited about —

    A   B   C   D   N

11. apparantly it has the world's longest coloured pencil. In the evening, we're going

    A   B   C   D   N

12. to a restaraunt and then to the theatre. I'm exhausted though. Hopefully, I won't

    A   B   C   D   N

13. fall asleep — we've received precise instructions to be on our best behavour!

    A   B   C   D   N

Love, Emma

END OF TEST

/ 18

You have **10 minutes** to do this test. Work as quickly and accurately as you can.

Read this passage carefully and answer the questions that follow.

An extract from 'What Katy Did at School'

"Oh! What is it? What has happened?" cried Clover, starting up in bed the next morning, as a clanging sound roused her suddenly from sleep. It was only the rising-bell, ringing at the end of Quaker Row.

Katy held her watch up to the dim light. She could just see the hands. Yes: they
5   pointed to six. It was actually morning! She and Clover jumped up, and began to dress as fast as possible.

"We've only got half an hour," said Clover, unhooking the rules, and carrying them to the window, — "Half an hour; and this says that we must turn the mattress, smooth the under-sheet over the bolster, and spend five minutes in silent devotion!
10 We'll have to be quick to do all that besides dressing ourselves!"

It is never easy to be quick, when one is in a hurry. Everything sets itself against you. Fingers turn into thumbs; dresses won't button, nor pins keep their place. With all their haste, Katy and Clover were barely ready when the second bell sounded. As they hastened downstairs, Katy fastening her breast-pin, and Clover her cuffs, they
15 met other girls, some looking half asleep, some half dressed; all yawning, rubbing their eyes, and complaining of the early hour.

"Isn't it horrid?" said Lilly Page, hurrying by with no collar on, and her hair hastily tucked into a net. "I never get up till nine o'clock when I'm at home. Ma saves my breakfast for me. She says I shall have my sleep out while I have the chance."

Susan Coolidge

Answer these questions about the text. You can refer back to the text if you need to.

1.   Give another word or phrase that means the same as
     "roused" (line 2) as it is used in the text.

2. Why does Clover have to unhook the rules and take them to the window?

_____

_____

3. By what time do the girls have to be ready?
   Tick the box next to the correct answer.

   A   6:00 am   ☐

   B   6:15 am   ☐

   C   6:30 am   ☐

   D   6:35 am   ☐

4. What does the author mean by "silent devotion" (line 9)?

   _____

5. Why do the girls find it difficult to get ready?
   Tick the box next to the correct answer.

   A   They only have half an hour.   ☐

   B   They are panicking.   ☐

   C   They are rushing too much.   ☐

   D   The buttons on their clothes won't fasten properly.   ☐

TURN OVER ➡

23 Test 8

6. What is the purpose of second bell? Tick the box next to the correct answer.

    A   To tell the girls it is time to go downstairs. ☐

    B   To tell the girls to turn their mattresses. ☐

    C   To tell the girls they are late. ☐

    D   To wake up the girls. ☐

7. Write down a word or phrase from the text that means "hurried".

_____

8. What do we learn about Clover from the text?
   Tick the box next to the correct answer.

    A   She takes a long time to get ready. ☐

    B   She doesn't like to break the rules. ☐

    C   She is untidy. ☐

    D   She doesn't like getting up early. ☐

9. "Ma saves my breakfast for me". Which word in this sentence is a preposition?
   Tick the box next to the correct answer.

    A   saves ☐

    B   my ☐

    C   for ☐

    D   me ☐

END OF TEST

/ 9

You have **10 minutes** to do this test. Work as quickly and accurately as you can.

> This passage contains some spelling mistakes.
> Write the passage out again with the correct spellings.

1. The weather forcast for tomorow has predicted severe snow for much of the
    country. It is recomended that only esential journies are made because the
    roads are likely to be trecherous.

    _____

    _____

    _____

> This passage has some punctuation mistakes.
> Write the passage out again with the correct punctuation.

2. Despite the road closure its still possible to go out. Put on some suitable shoes (such
    as walking boots, leave in good time, and walk rather than drive

    _____

    _____

    _____

TURN OVER ➡

For each numbered line, choose the word which completes the passage correctly. The passage needs to make sense and be written in correct English. Circle the correct letter.

3. Dachshunds **is are were was am** a popular pet among dog lovers. With their
   A B C D E

4. elongated bodies and tiny features, **these those this that they** are hard to resist.
   A B C D E

5. **They're Their There Her Than** name comes from the German for "badger dog",
   A B C D E

6. as they were originally bred **as to from for which** hunting badgers. But today,
   A B C D E

   they are more likely to be seen frequenting a park, and their distinctive shape

7. **has have is having are** earned them the nickname "sausage dog". These little
   A B C D E

8. dogs **showed shown show shows showing** a lot of affection.
   A B C D E

9. **Whereas Whichever However While Whereupon** , they can be a bit stubborn,
   A B C D E

10. **who what where which when** can make training them a challenge.
    A B C D E

END OF TEST

/ 18

Puzzles 3

Let's pause for some puzzles that will put your **word** skills to the test.

Crossword Contest

Complete the crossword by choosing an appropriate synonym for each word below.

ACROSS

2. Complete
4. Concentrate
7. Victory
8. Discover
11. Impolite
12. Announce

DOWN

1. Nimble
3. Friendly
5. Shortly
6. Respect
9. Conquer
10. Close

Odd One Out

All of these words except one have a similar meaning. Find the odd one out, then rearrange all the letters in the shaded squares to find a synonym of the word which is the odd one out.

S C A R E D   F E A R F U L   I N D I G N A N T

T E R R I F I E D   F R I G H T E N E D

Hidden word: _ _ _ _ _ _ _ _ _ _

You have **10 minutes** to do this test. Work as quickly and accurately as you can.

For each numbered line, choose the word, or group of words,
which completes the passage correctly. The passage needs to make
sense and be written in correct English. Circle the correct letter.

1. My dad **takes** **take** **brings** **took** **taken** me to watch our local team play
         A   B   C   D   E

2. football today. I **aren't** **am** **wasn't** **weren't** **was** sure if I'd enjoy it, but we
         A   B   C   D   E

3. had a great time **standing** **standed** **stands** **stand** **stooding** on the terraces. I
         A   B   C   D   E

4. think I **ought to** **would have** **will have** **should have** **must have** to go again.
         A   B   C   D   E

This passage contains some spelling mistakes.
Write the passage out again with the correct spellings.

5. Having recently been referbished, 'Joy's Food Emporium' is now open again for
    buisness. Refreshmants are availabel as usual, including our fammous pints of tea,
    as well as some delicous new creations.

    _____

    _____

    _____

    _____

This passage contains some punctuation mistakes. Each numbered line has either one mistake or no mistake. For each line, work out which group of words contains a mistake, and circle the letter. Circle N if there is no mistake.

6. Locals walking the streets of Woollerton were in for another surprise yesterday

   A **B** **C** **D** **N**

7. morning. More unexplained-knitting appeared in the town overnight. For the

   A **B** **C** **D** **N**

8. third time this week, objects such as lampposts bollards and benches have

   A **B** **C** **D** **N**

9. found themselves, wearing colourful, yet tasteful, knitted items. Residents are

   A **B** **C** **D** **N**

10. enjoying this woollen art. Mrs Needleby said this morning, "it's much nicer

    A **B** **C** **D** **N**

11. than graffiti. Mr Hatton, a shop owner, claims that people are taking the hats on

    A **B** **C** **D** **N**

12. the bollards home to use as tea cosies; only for more to appear a few days later.

    A **B** **C** **D** **N**

13. Woollerton will soon be as fashionable as all of it's inhabitants this winter.

    A **B** **C** **D** **N**

END OF TEST

/ 18

You have **10 minutes** to do this test. Work as quickly and accurately as you can.

Read this passage carefully and answer the questions that follow.

The Song of the Camp

"Give us a song!" the soldiers cried,
The outer trenches guarding,
When the heated guns of the camps allied
Grew weary of bombarding.

5   The dark Redan*, in silent scoff,
Lay, grim and threatening, under;
And the tawny mound of the Malakoff*
No longer belched its thunder.

There was a pause. A guardsman said,
10 "We storm the forts to-morrow;
Sing while we may, another day
Will bring enough of sorrow."

They lay along the battery's side,
Below the smoking cannon:
15 Brave hearts, from Severn and from Clyde,
And from the banks of Shannon.

They sang of love, and not of fame;
Forgot was Britain's glory:
Each heart recalled a different name,
20 But all sang "Annie Laurie."

Voice after voice caught up the song,
Until its tender passion
Rose like an anthem, rich and strong, —
Their battle-eve confession.

25 Dear girl, her name he dared not speak,
But, as the song grew louder,
Something upon the soldier's cheek
Washed off the stains of powder.

Beyond the darkening ocean burned
30 The bloody sunset's embers,
While the Crimean valleys learned
How English love remembers.

And once again a fire of hell
Rained on the Russian quarters,
35 With scream of shot, and burst of shell,
And bellowing of the mortars!

And Irish Nora's eyes are dim
For a singer, dumb and gory;
And English Mary mourns for him
40 Who sang of "Annie Laurie."

Sleep, soldiers! still in honoured rest
Your truth and valour wearing:
The bravest are the tenderest, —
The loving are the daring.

Bayard Taylor

* Redan — *an arrow-shaped part of a fort*
* Malakoff — *the name of a fort*

Answer these questions about the text. You can refer back to the text if you need to.

1. The guns have been firing for a long time.
   What information in the poem tells you this?

   _____

   _____

2. "silent scoff" (line 5). What is this phrase an example of?
   Tick the box next to the correct answer.

   A   A metaphor   ☐

   B   Alliteration   ☐

   C   Rhyme   ☐

   D   A simile   ☐

3. Which country are the "Brave hearts" (line 15) fighting for?

   _____

4. "Rose like an anthem, rich and strong, —
   Their battle-eve confession." (Lines 23-24). Which word in this sentence is a verb?
   Tick the box next to the correct answer.

   A   Rose   ☐

   B   anthem   ☐

   C   strong   ☐

   D   Their   ☐

TURN OVER ➡

5. What "Washed off the stains of powder" (line 28) from the soldier's cheek?

_____

6. Where is the battle taking place?
   Tick the box next to the correct answer.

   A   In Shannon   ☐

   B   In Britain   ☐

   C   In Crimea   ☐

   D   In England   ☐

7. According to the text, how do Irish Nora and English Mary feel?

_____

8. Which are the only soldiers to sleep during the battle?

_____

9. Give another word or phrase that means the same as "valour" (line 42) as it is used in the text.

_____

END OF TEST

/ 9

You have **10 minutes** to do this test. Work as quickly and accurately as you can.

> For each numbered line, choose the word, or group of words, which completes the passage correctly. The passage needs to make sense and be written in correct English. Circle the correct letter.

1. The moon was **rosed** **rised** **raising** **riseing** **rising** above the dark blue
              A   **B**   **C**   **D**   **E**

2. sea. Leo **sinks** **sunked** **sank** **sink** **sinked** his toes into the sand as he watched
             A   **B**   **C**   **D**   **E**

3. the ship in the distance come steadily **near** **close** **nearer** **further** **far**.
                        A   **B**   **C**   **D**   **E**

4. He **could have** **couldn't do** **could** **could do** **couldn't have** nothing now,
            A   **B**   **C**   **D**   **E**

except wait to be rescued.

> This passage has some punctuation mistakes.
> Write the passage out again with the correct punctuation.

5. This lighthouse famous for its multicoloured paintwork is open to the public for the
    first time at the heart of many dramatic rescues it has a fascinating story to tell

    _____

    _____

    _____

TURN OVER ➡

This passage contains some spelling mistakes. Each numbered line has either one mistake or no mistake. For each line, work out which group of words contains a mistake, and circle the correct letter. Circle N if there is no mistake.

6. Sasha leept off her sled into the powdery snow. Snowflakes whirled around

    A   B   C   D   N

7. her head as she retreived her bow and arrows, and walked into the forest.

    A   B   C   D   N

8. Hunting was her speciallity. She was highly skilled, and she enjoyed having

    A   B   C   D   N

9. the responsibility of making sure the inhabitents of her village had enough food

    A   B   C   D   N

10. to get through the winter. Unfortunately, there had been a curious absense of

    A   B   C   D   N

11. wildlife in the forest lately. Legend had it that all animals dissappeared when an

    A   B   C   D   N

12. avalanche was on its way, but no one really believed it. Sasha couldn't

    A   B   C   D   N

13. help but feel anxious though — the forest seemed unaturally still and quiet.

    A   B   C   D   N

END OF TEST

/ 18

Puzzles 4

Time for something a bit different. Test your **spelling** skills with these puzzles.

Treasure Trail

Underline the spelling mistakes in the clues below, and write the correct spelling on the line. Then follow the clues using the map on the right. Write down how many coins you collect along the way.

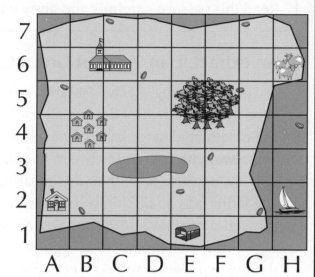

a) Start at the blue manner house.
_____

b) Walk rite briskly for seven squares.
_____

c) Sale north across stormy seas for four squares. _____

d) Go west through the heard of cows, and carry on for four squares. _____

e) Travel south over baron land until you reach the lake. _____

How many coins did you collect? _____

Country Confusion

Unscramble these letters to find the names of three countries.

Then rearrange the letters in the shaded boxes to find a hidden country.

D L S T C A O N   T K I N A S A P   O G R L T U P A

_____   _____   _____

Hidden country: _ _ _ _ _ _

Puzzles 4

You have **10 minutes** to do this test. Work as quickly and accurately as you can.

Read this passage carefully and answer the questions that follow.

An extract from 'Anne of Green Gables'

"Good evening, Rachel," Marilla said briskly. "This is a real fine evening, isn't it? Won't you sit down? How are all your folks?"

Something that for lack of any other name might be called friendship existed and always had existed between Marilla Cuthbert and Mrs Rachel, in spite of — or
5   perhaps because of — their dissimilarity.

Marilla was a tall, thin woman, with angles and without curves; her dark hair showed some gray streaks and was always twisted up in a hard little knot behind with two wire hairpins stuck aggressively through it. She looked like a woman of narrow experience and rigid conscience, which she was; but there was a saving
10   something about her mouth which, if it had been ever so slightly developed, might have been considered indicative of a sense of humor.

"We're all pretty well," said Mrs Rachel. "I was kind of afraid YOU weren't, though, when I saw Matthew starting off today. I thought maybe he was going to the doctor's."
15   Marilla's lips twitched understandingly. She had expected Mrs Rachel up; she had known that the sight of Matthew jaunting off so unaccountably would be too much for her neighbor's curiosity.

"Oh, no, I'm quite well although I had a bad headache yesterday," she said. "Matthew went to Bright River. We're getting a little boy from an orphan asylum in
20   Nova Scotia and he's coming on the train tonight."

If Marilla had said that Matthew had gone to Bright River to meet a kangaroo from Australia Mrs Rachel could not have been more astonished. She was actually stricken dumb for five seconds. It was unsupposable that Marilla was making fun of her, but Mrs Rachel was almost forced to suppose it.

Lucy Maud Montgomery

Answer these questions about the text. You can refer back to the text if you need to.

1. In your own words, describe the relationship between Rachel and Marilla.

   _____

   _____

2. Give another word or phrase that means the same as
   "dissimilarity" (line 5) as it is used in the text.

   _____

3. What does the phrase "narrow experience and rigid conscience" (line 9) tell us
   about Marilla's personality?

   _____

   _____

4. According to the text, which of the following is Marilla's one redeeming feature?
   Tick the box next to the correct answer.

   A   Her mouth   ☐

   B   Her height   ☐

   C   Her figure   ☐

   D   Her hair   ☐

TURN OVER ➡

5. What do you think is the purpose of Rachel's visit?
    Tick the box next to the correct answer.

    A   She was concerned about Marilla being ill. ☐

    B   She was concerned about Matthew being ill. ☐

    C   She wanted to know where Matthew was going. ☐

    D   She wanted to talk to Marilla about the boy she was adopting. ☐

6. "the sight of Matthew jaunting off so unaccountably" (line 16).
    Which of these words is a verb?

    _____

7. Why had Matthew gone to Bright River?

    _____

8. Which of the words below is closest in meaning to the word "astonished" (line 22)?
    Tick the box next to the correct answer.

    A   Appalled   ☐

    B   Disturbed ☐

    C   Shocked   ☐

    D   Alarmed   ☐

9. Why is Rachel almost forced to suppose that Marilla was making fun of her?
    Tick the box next to the correct answer.

    A   Marilla has never discussed adopting a child with her before. ☐

    B   Marilla making fun of her is more believable than her adopting a child. ☐

    C   She doesn't want to believe that Marilla has adopted a child. ☐

    D   She thinks Marilla is lying to her. ☐

END OF TEST

/ 9

(10)

You have **10 minutes** to do this test. Work as quickly and accurately as you can.

> This passage contains some spelling mistakes.
> Write the passage out again with the correct spellings.

1. Keeping hens is a rewarding hobbie, especially if you rescue them from a battery
    farm, because you'll have the satisfactian of knowing you've given an animal
    the oportunity of a better existance.

    _____

    _____

    _____

    _____

> This passage has some punctuation mistakes.
> Write the passage out again with the correct punctuation.

2. Great shouted Jeff glaring upwards as the traffic lights turned to red he'd been late
    yesterday as well, so he couldn't believe it was happening again.

    _____

    _____

    _____

TURN OVER ➡

For each numbered line, choose the word which completes the passage correctly. The passage needs to make sense and be written in correct English. Circle the correct letter.

3. Jo stopped swimming and paused **on through in onto at** the water.
   A   B   C   D   E

4. She **might could may couldn't had** only just see the island in the distance
   A   B   C   D   E

5. which meant she still had a **lengthy breadth length long longest** way to go.
   A   B   C   D   E

6. Even though she **what were where was wasn't** wearing a wet suit, the cold still
   A   B   C   D   E

7. bit at her body. She was beginning to doubt **if when as which what** she
   A   B   C   D   E

   would make it to the island and finish the race. Many competitors were starting to

8. swim **passed past pass passing passes** her now. She couldn't let this happen.
   A   B   C   D   E

9. She **has hadn't haven't have had** trained too hard to give up now. She gritted
   A   B   C   D   E

10. her teeth determinedly and **begin begins began begun beginning** to swim.
    A   B   C   D   E

END OF TEST

/ 18

Test 15: Comprehension

You have **10 minutes** to do this test. Work as quickly and accurately as you can.

Read this passage carefully and answer the questions that follow.

Stonehenge

Located on the Salisbury Plain in the south of England, Stonehenge is one of the most famous prehistoric monuments in the world. The large standing stones arranged in rings that form Stonehenge provide a unique insight into prehistoric times. For this reason, many have fought for its protection, and it has been awarded
5 World Heritage Site status.

Stonehenge was built in several stages between 3000 BC and 2000 BC, but unfortunately there are no written records from this time. While we know the monument consists of different types of stone, historians are unsure about how our ancestors transported these stones to Salisbury. Large sarsen stones, up to 40
10 tonnes in weight, were taken from quarries 25 miles away, and bluestones, which weigh around 4 tonnes, originated from Wales, around 150 miles away. Historians and visitors alike are amazed that people with such limited technology managed to transport and arrange the stones in this way.

Stonehenge's purpose is steeped in mystery: some believe it was a place of
15 healing because bluestones were thought to have curative powers; others claim it is a burial site for royalty; some even maintain that it was once a Druid temple. These theories and many others have caused much speculation.

Unfortunately, over the years, some of the stones have collapsed and suffered erosion. When Stonehenge first opened to the public, visitors were allowed to walk
20 among the stones, but they have now been cordoned off. Despite this, Stonehenge remains a popular tourist attraction, with nearly one million visitors each year. However, its popularity has alarmed some people. There are growing concerns that the proximity of major roads to the monument will spoil what was originally a peaceful and undisturbed historical site.

TURN OVER ➡

Answer these questions about the text. You can refer back to the text if you need to.

1. Why do many people think that Stonehenge deserves special protection?
   Tick the box next to the correct answer.

   A   Because it is a World Heritage Site ☐

   B   Because it is arranged in an unusual shape ☐

   C   Because it tells us a lot about prehistoric times ☐

   D   Because it is very famous ☐

2. Explain the meaning of the phrase "unique insight" (line 3) as it is used in the text.

   _____

   _____

3. Why can't historians be sure about how the stone was transported?

   _____

4. What is it about the building of Stonehenge that has "amazed" historians?
   Tick the box next to the correct answer.

   A   The stones used were very rare. ☐

   B   The people who built it didn't have advanced machinery or transport. ☐

   C   The large variety of stones used. ☐

   D   The building of the monument was such a long process. ☐

5. What makes people think that Stonehenge was a place for curing illnesses?

   _____

6. Find a noun in the text that means "conjecture".

    _____

7. Which of the following is not mentioned in the text?
    Tick the box next to the correct answer.

    A   Some people believe the noise from cars affects the site. ☐

    B   Stonehenge's sarsen stones were quarried in Wales. ☐

    C   Why Stonehenge was built still remains a mystery. ☐

    D   Stonehenge receives a high number of visitors. ☐

8. "When Stonehenge first opened to the public, visitors were allowed to walk among
    the stones, but they have now been cordoned off." (lines 19-20).
    Which of these words is a preposition? Tick the box next to the correct answer.

    A   cordoned   ☐

    B   first   ☐

    C   among   ☐

    D   visitors   ☐

9. "peaceful" and "undisturbed" as they are used in the text are examples of which
    type of word? Tick the box next to the correct answer.

    A   Verb   ☐

    B   Adverb   ☐

    C   Adjective   ☐

    D   Noun   ☐

    END OF TEST

    / 9

Puzzles 5

Phew! That's another batch of tests completed. Now let's exercise your **word type** skills.

Verbsearch

Circle 5 verbs and 5 adverbs in the grid. Then write each word under the correct heading in the table below. The first letter of each word has been given to help you.

Verb	Adverb
a....................	a....................
d....................	f....................
f....................	g....................
h....................	o....................
p....................	s....................

A	Y	L	R	A	O	Z	C	E
F	L	P	E	C	L	Y	A	E
I	R	Y	A	H	G	W	S	R
E	Y	F	L	I	E	N	E	G
R	L	B	W	E	N	E	U	A
C	T	S	A	V	T	T	F	S
E	F	I	Y	E	L	F	A	I
L	I	D	S	A	Y	O	M	D
Y	W	H	E	L	P	B	A	O
B	S	A	N	E	E	E	L	F

Balloon Bedlam

Reunite the babies with their balloons by drawing a line from the words in the balloons to the type of word they are.

they   onto   greed   you   and   healthy   wise   or   among   wealth

Adjective   Pronoun   Preposition   Conjunction   Noun

10

You have **10 minutes** to do this test. Work as quickly and accurately as you can.

> For each numbered line, choose the word, or group of words,
> which completes the passage correctly. The passage needs to make
> sense and be written in correct English. Circle the correct letter.

1. Richard believed there was **lots a lot more much great** to life than just work.
                                       A   B   C   D   E

2. He enjoyed **been being for be to** able to do as he pleased on his days off,
                         A   B   C   D E

3. when he **could likes has will had** take long walks with his dog.
                   A   B   C   D   E

4. Richard wished that **all most to whole every** day was his day off.
                            A   B   C   D   E

> This passage contains some spelling mistakes.
> Write the passage out again with the correct spellings.

5. Dawn was having trouble decideing witch new car to perchase. She wanted
    something ecanomical, but because she was on a very tight budgit, her options
    were quiet limited.

    _____

    _____

    _____

    _____

TURN OVER ➡

        45

This passage contains some punctuation mistakes. Each numbered line has either one mistake or no mistake. For each line, work out which group of words contains a mistake, and circle the correct letter. Circle N if there is no mistake.

6. It was the last day of term before the summer holiday's at the high school.

   A   **B**   **C**   **D**   **N**

7. Mr Smiths students were all anxious for the end of the day, after which they

   A   **B**   **C**   **D**   **N**

8. would have a six week break from school. Many of the students were excited

   A   **B**   **C**   **D**   **N**

9. about going on holiday but some were just looking forward to relaxing without

   A   **B**   **C**   **D**   **N**

10. having any school work to think about. Mr Smith was having some trouble

   A   **B**   **C**   **D**   **N**

11. keeping the students focused on their work No matter how many times he told

   A   **B**   **C**   **D**   **N**

12. the class to be quiet, they kept talking about their plans for the summer holidays.

   A   **B**   **C**   **D**   **N**

13. "I give up! he sighed exasperatedly, "Just have the rest of the lesson off."

   A   **B**   **C**   **D**   **N**

END OF TEST

/ 18

You have **10 minutes** to do this test. Work as quickly and accurately as you can.

Read this passage carefully and answer the questions that follow.

The Photograph

Ellie made her way up the winding lane, through the gate to the fields, and followed the track she habitually took. She took pleasure in her meandering strolls, but today's walk was filled with purpose: she needed to catch an animal on camera for a wildlife project at school. The sun's rays warmed the afternoon, yet Ellie felt a
5   shiver engulf her as the path took her through the copse, and the sun gave way to the leafy canopy.

A bird caught her attention, drawing her eye to a path she had never seen before. It cut through the trees and up the hillside, and, seized by curiosity, Ellie decided to follow it. The way became gradually steeper, and soon she was using her hands
10 to scramble, her lungs and legs burning. Upon arriving at the top, a crater-shaped hollow was revealed, in the bottom of which lay a small body of water, black and deathly still. She watched, mesmerised, as ripples began to disturb the surface. These grew larger, and a pounding roar ripped through the peaceful afternoon. Something suddenly broke the water's surface: it resembled a monstrous creature,
15 despite being partly obscured by the churning water. Ellie hurriedly grappled for her camera, captured the scene with trembling hands, and fled back down the hillside.

The moment she arrived home, she shouted to her parents. "Look! Look what I've just seen!" She grabbed her camera, oscillating wildly between feelings of excitement and fear. Looking down at the display, her feelings of excitement rapidly
20 turned to shock when she saw the picture she had just taken, for nothing met her eyes except the smooth silky surface of an eerily still pond.

Answer the following questions about the text. You can refer back to the text if you need to.

TURN OVER ➡

1. Explain one way in which Ellie's walk differs from her usual walk.

_____

2. What makes Ellie shiver? Tick the box next to the correct answer.

   A   She's scared of what she is about to see.   ☐

   B   She's excited about photographing a rare animal.   ☐

   C   The sun isn't providing much warmth.   ☐

   D   The shade of the trees makes her cold.   ☐

3. Why does Ellie decide to take the path up the hill?
   Tick the box next to the correct answer.

   A   She wants to photograph the bird.   ☐

   B   She is bored with her habitual walk.   ☐

   C   She is interested in the path as she has never noticed it before.   ☐

   D   She thinks there will be more animals to photograph on the hill.   ☐

4. Where does Ellie come across the creature?
   Tick the box next to the correct answer.

   A   In the woodland   ☐

   B   In a small pool   ☐

   C   At the bottom of the hill   ☐

   D   On the hillside   ☐

5. Which of the words below is closest in meaning to the word
   "obscured" (line 15)? Tick the box next to the correct answer.

   A   Exposed   ☐

   B   Enclosed   ☐

   C   Concealed   ☐

   D   Invisible   ☐

6. "The moment she arrived home, she shouted to her parents." (Line 17). Which of these words is the subject of the sentence? Tick the box next to the correct answer.

    A   home ☐

    B   her parents ☐

    C   she ☐

    D   The moment ☐

7. Give another word or phrase that means the same as "oscillating" (line 18) as it is used in the text.

_____

8. How does Ellie feel when she looks at the photograph she has taken? Tick the box next to the correct answer.

    A   Disappointed ☐

    B   Frustrated ☐

    C   Delighted ☐

    D   Astounded ☐

9. Find a phrase from the text that contains alliteration.

_____

END OF TEST

/ 9

         49

You have **10 minutes** to do this test. Work as quickly and accurately as you can.

> For each numbered line, choose the word, or group of words,
> which completes the passage correctly. The passage needs to make
> sense and be written in correct English. Circle the correct letter.

1. The two girls **ridden** **rode** **rided** **have ridden** **rides** their bikes through the field.
         A   B   C   D   E

2. The field **were** **being** **was** **is** **was not** deserted apart from the girls and an
         A   B   C   D   E

3. elderly man and woman walking **there** **they're** **her** **their** **them** dog. The two
         A   B   C   D   E

4. girls cycled away from **when** **were** **why** **wear** **where** they were walking.
         A   B   C   D   E

> This passage has some punctuation mistakes.
> Write the passage out again with the correct punctuation.

5. To make Yorkshire puddings mix flour eggs and milk in a bowl Heat some oil in the
    Yorkshire pudding tin's, then add the mixture to the tins dividing it equally between
    them. cook for 20 minutes.

    _____

    _____

    _____

    _____

This passage contains some spelling mistakes. Each numbered line has either one mistake or no mistake. For each line, work out which group of words contains a mistake, and circle the correct letter. Circle N if there is no mistake.

6. Amy stepped warily through the front gates of her new school, anxious about her

   A　　　　　**B**　　　　　**C**　　　　　**D**　　　**N**

7. first day there. The building loomed over her as she huried through the playground

   A　　　　　**B**　　　　　**C**　　　　　**D**　　　**N**

8. towards the main entranse. Several older students stood huddled in small groups,

   A　　　　　**B**　　　　　**C**　　　　　**D**　　　**N**

9. staring at her. Amy lengthend her stride, hastening to get away from them.

   A　　　　　**B**　　　　　**C**　　　　　**D**　　　**N**

10. She eventualy reached the heavy front doors, only to find her way obstructed by a

   A　　　　　**B**　　　　　**C**　　　　　**D**　　　**N**

11. tall, burly boy who smirked at her. "Get out of the way!" Amy demanded, faigning

   A　　　　　**B**　　　　　**C**　　　　　**D**　　　**N**

12. confidance. The boy's smirk disappeared as he moved aside reluctantly, letting

   A　　　　　**B**　　　　　**C**　　　　　**D**　　　**N**

13. Amy pass. She marched through the doors, feeling a little better about her first day.

   A　　　　　**B**　　　　　**C**　　　　　**D**　　　**N**

END OF TEST

/ 18

Puzzles 6

Time for a break! These puzzles are a great way to practise your **word type** skills.

Place the Word Types

Draw a line from each word to its correct place in the sentence. When the words are in the right order, the shaded letters will spell out a new word.

P L A Y E D   F L U F F Y   A N D

The [adjective] cat [conjunction] the friendly [noun]

[verb] [adverb] with the mouse [preposition] the garden.

I N   C A R E F U L L Y   P O O D L E

New word: _ _ _ _ _ _ _

Word Type Scramble

Unscramble each anagram — each one is a synonym of the word next to it in brackets. Then write the word type on the line. The first one's been done for you.

OSUROMNE (big)   E N O R M O U S   ....adjective..........

LITASHY (quickly)   ☐☐☐☐☐☐☐   ....

EDRATP (leave)   ☐☐☐☐☐☐   ....

OVABE (over)   ☐☐☐☐☐   ....

IUFROSU (angry)   ☐☐☐☐☐☐☐   ....

You have **10 minutes** to do this test. Work as quickly and accurately as you can.

> Read this passage carefully and answer the questions that follow.

I Wandered Lonely as a Cloud

I wandered lonely as a cloud
That floats on high o'er vales and hills,
When all at once I saw a crowd,
A host, of golden daffodils;
5 Beside the lake, beneath the trees,
Fluttering and dancing in the breeze.

Continuous as the stars that shine
And twinkle on the milky way,
They stretched in never-ending line
10 Along the margin of a bay:
Ten thousand saw I at a glance,
Tossing their heads in sprightly dance.

The waves beside them danced; but they
Out-did the sparkling waves in glee:
15 A poet could not but be gay,
In such a jocund* company:
I gazed — and gazed — but little thought
What wealth the show to me had brought:

For oft, when on my couch I lie
20 In vacant or in pensive mood,
They flash upon that inward eye
Which is the bliss of solitude;
And then my heart with pleasure fills,
And dances with the daffodils.

William Wordsworth

* jocund — *cheerful*

> Answer these questions about the text. You can refer back to the text if you need to.

1.   Find a phrase from the text that contains a simile.

_____

TURN OVER ➡

2. According to the poem, where are the daffodils not located?
    Tick the box next to the correct answer.

    A   Under the trees   ☐

    B   On the hills   ☐

    C   Next to the lake   ☐

    D   Beside the bay   ☐

3. "dancing in the breeze" (line 6). What is this phrase an example of?
    Tick the box next to the correct answer.

    A   Simile   ☐

    B   Alliteration   ☐

    C   Metaphor   ☐

    D   Personification   ☐

4. "Continuous as the stars that shine / And twinkle on the milky way," (lines 7-8).
    What do these lines mean? Tick the box next to the correct answer.

    A   The daffodils are twinkling and shining.   ☐

    B   The daffodils appear to stretch as far as the stars.   ☐

    C   The daffodils look like stars.   ☐

    D   The daffodils will live as long as the stars.   ☐

5. Which of these statements is false? Tick the box next to the correct answer.

    A   The waves are more joyful than the daffodils.   ☐

    B   There is a large number of daffodils.   ☐

    C   The daffodils are swaying in the wind.   ☐

    D   The daffodils make the poet content.   ☐

6. What type of word is "beside" (line 13)?

_____

7. "I gazed — and gazed — but little thought / What wealth the show to me had brought" (lines 17-18). Explain what these lines mean in your own words.

_____

_____

8. Explain what the author means by "They flash upon that inward eye" (line 21).

_____

_____

9. Which of these words is closest in meaning to "solitude" (line 22)?
    Tick the box next to the correct answer.

    A   Solidarity   ☐

    B   Isolation   ☐

    C   Solemnity   ☐

    D   Lethargy   ☐

END OF TEST

/ 9

You have **10 minutes** to do this test. Work as quickly and accurately as you can.

Read this passage carefully and answer the questions that follow.

Man versus Horse Marathon

If you have ever wondered who would win a race between a horse and a human, the best place to go is Llanwrtyd Wells — a small town in Wales where the Man versus Horse Marathon is held annually.

In the 1970s, local businessmen in Llanwrtyd Wells wanted to find ways to boost
5   the local tourist economy. Gordon Green, a pub landlord, overheard two men talking one evening, and he spotted an opportunity. One man boldly suggested that humans were equal to any horse over long distances and on cross-country terrain. His friend challenged him to prove it. Green decided to take the helm, and he made it a public event which would begin in the town centre.

10   The first race was held in 1980. It was 22 miles in length, and it challenged competitors over a variety of terrains: hills, marsh and track. The horses were easily victorious, but after the course was altered two years later, the race became a much closer contest. Despite this, equine competitors continued to retain the upper hand. However, the twenty-fifth anniversary of the race proved to be a momentous
15   occasion when elite marathon runner, Huw Lobb, reached the finish line two minutes before the first horse. The reward for his triumph was £25,000.

While it's true that horses possess the advantage when it comes to speed, humans tend to have superior endurance and a higher tolerance of rough terrain. Horses are also susceptible to overheating, and consequently, they are obliged to take a ten- to
20   fifteen-minute break during the race. It's no coincidence, therefore, that when Lobb won the race, it was a hot day. The fact that it took an elite marathon runner to beat the horses, however, does not fill the average runner with confidence. In fact, only two humans have defeated the horses since Lobb's victory — both in 2007.

Answer these questions about the text. You can refer back to the text if you need to.

1. Why was it bold of one of the men to suggest that "humans were equal to any horse over long distances and on cross-country terrain" (line 7)?

    _____

    _____

2. Why do you think the starting point of the race was in the town centre?

    _____

    _____

3. Explain the meaning of the phrase "take the helm" (line 8) as it is used in the text.

    _____

4. What happened in 1982 that helped humans stand a better chance of winning the race? Tick the box next to the correct answer.

    A   Horses were made to take breaks.   ☐

    B   The route was modified.   ☐

    C   Elite runners were allowed to enter.   ☐

    D   The race was held on a hot day.   ☐

TURN OVER ➡

5. Which of the following statements is false? Tick the box next to the correct answer.

    A   Horses can run for longer periods than humans. ☐

    B   Horses can run faster than humans. ☐

    C   Humans can withstand higher temperatures than horses. ☐

    D   Horses may struggle to run on hills. ☐

6. Give another word or phrase that means the same as "susceptible" (line 19) as it is used in the text.

    _____

7. "Horses are also susceptible to overheating, and consequently, they are obliged to take a ten- to fifteen-minute break during the race." (Lines 18-20). Which word in this sentence is a pronoun? Tick the box next to the correct answer.

    A   are ☐

    B   to ☐

    C   they ☐

    D   during ☐

8. Why was it not a coincidence that Lobb won the race on a hot day?

    _____

    _____

9. Why does Lobb's achievement not fill most runners with optimism?

    _____

    _____

END OF TEST

    / 9

Test 21: Proofreading

You have **10 minutes** to do this test. Work as quickly and accurately as you can.

> This passage contains some spelling mistakes.
> Write the passage out again with the correct spellings.

1. "This steak is marvallous," Frances said to George, in their favourite Italiun restaurant. "Is your chicken nice?" she asked. George nodded enthusiasticaly, unnable to speak through a mouthfull of food.

_____

_____

_____

_____

> This passage has some punctuation mistakes.
> Write the passage out again with the correct punctuation.

2. "Its so busy! yelled Natalie Tariq and Rosie simultaneously, staring through the shops window Everyone was desperate to take advantage of the half-price sale.

_____

_____

_____

_____

TURN OVER ➡

For each numbered line, choose the word, or group of words, which completes the passage correctly. The passage needs to make sense and be written in correct English. Circle the correct letter.

3. The ancient house that sat atop the hill **were** **is** **where** **was** **has** rumoured
                    A   B   C   D   E

4. to be haunted. Kieran **could** **would** **couldn't** **will** **should** resist an adventure
            A   B   C   D   E

5. like this, so he wandered **over** **towards** **below** **at** **beyond** to the house
            A   B   C   D   E

6. to investigate. He **knows** **knowed** **new** **knew** **has known** he wasn't
           A   B   C   D   E

7. supposed to visit the house, so he crept discreetly up to **it's** **isn't** **it** **its** **is** front
                        A   B   C   D E

    door, finding it slightly ajar. Kieran entered the house and came across a dusty

8. hallway, which was empty **apart** **expect** **except** **from** **accept** for an old
             A   B   C   D   E

    wardrobe that was rattling. Kieran hesitated, but then slowly began to creep

9. **further** **farthest** **far** **father** **furthest** down the hall. Suddenly, the front door
      A   B   C   D   E

10. slammed shut, and he **herd** **heard** **hear** **hears** **heared** a key turn in the lock.
             A   B   C   D   E

END OF TEST

/ 18

Have a go at these puzzles to test your knowledge of **spelling** and **descriptive language**.

Spelling Secrets

David and Leah are planning a secret meeting. Leah has hidden the time of the meeting in the message below — the number of spelling mistakes gives the time of the meeting. Read the message and work out when the meeting is.

This morning, I went for
an extremelly long walk.
I went threw the fields
and towards the forrest.
Then when I got home, I
peruzed my favourite book.

_____ o'clock

Literary Link-up

Match each type of descriptive language to the correct sentence on the right.

metaphor

personification

alliteration

simile

The water was as clear
as a polished crystal.

The water was a handful of crystals
as it smashed over the rocks.

The water was chattering and
gurgling over the pebbles.

The water was whirling and
wheeling down the waterfall.

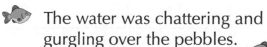

You have **10 minutes** to do this test. Work as quickly and accurately as you can.

For each numbered line, choose the word, or group of words, which completes the passage correctly. The passage needs to make sense and be written in correct English. Circle the correct letter.

1. Dad says he **should** **shouldve** **should have** **should've have** **should of**
             A   B   C   D   E

2. planned ahead, and **though** **threw** **through** **thought** **throughout** to cover
             A   B   C   D   E

3. the swimming pool **by** **before** **with** **in** **past** the storm hit. Now it's full of
             A   B   C   D   E

4. leaves and bits of tree, **witch** **where** **who** **which** **what** take ages to remove.
             A   B   C   D   E

This passage contains some spelling mistakes.
Write the passage out again with the correct spellings.

5. Our babysitter is a compleet bore. She sits idly on the sofa the hole time, and makes us endure teidous television programes instead of entertaining us. She's so misrable that it's a releif when she leaves.

_____

_____

_____

_____

This passage contains some punctuation mistakes. Each numbered line has either one mistake or no mistake. For each line, work out which group of words contains a mistake, and circle the correct letter. Circle N if there is no mistake.

6. Our youth orchestra rehearses three days a week: on Tuesdays Wednesdays and

    A   **B**   **C**   **D**   **N**

7. Fridays. We used to only rehearse twice, but were preparing for a performance

    A   **B**   **C**   **D**   **N**

8. at the moment, so our conductor (Mr Speaksworth has allowed extra time.

    A   **B**   **C**   **D**   **N**

9. There are four main sections in the orchestra: strings brass, percussion and

    A   **B**   **C**   **D**   **N**

10. woodwind. I'm in the woodwind section with my friend Kirsten because, we

    A   **B**   **C**   **D**   **N**

11. both play the flute. My favourite piece in the performance is called 'The Little

    A   **B**   **C**   **D**   **N**

12. Robin's Song because I have a solo in that one. I'm getting a bit nervous about

    A   **B**   **C**   **D**   **N**

13. it now, but as Mr Speaksworth always says, "it'll be alright on the night!"

    A   **B**   **C**   **D**   **N**

END OF TEST

/ 18

You have **10 minutes** to do this test. Work as quickly and accurately as you can.

> Read this passage carefully and answer the questions that follow.

The Farmhouse

Until they crested the ridge, where the view of it was clearer than it had been from the road, it had escaped Lowri's notice that she had already been to the old farmhouse. From this vantage point, the crumbling structure drew the eye; the only hint of human existence on a vast and desolate landscape of hills and valleys.

5 Now, instead of fleeting glimpses of a building as the road snaked eastwards and westwards and eastwards again, the farmhouse could be seen in its entirety, and like a familiar face, it roused a sense of recognition in Lowri.

"I know this place," she said quietly.

Descending from the ridge, ignoring her colleague's protests (the hour was late,
10 the equipment heavy, and this was an unwelcome detour), Lowri crossed the field towards the farmhouse. The metal front gate still stood intact, though most of the wall on either side had not been so fortunate. Nonetheless, she worked the gate, being sure to close it behind her, in response to Mrs Josephine's echoed insistence.

Lowri soon found herself in the kitchen. A shaft of sunlight shone through the
15 window at the far end, spotlighting the dust on the broad oak table. A pity — Mrs Josephine was a stickler for cleanliness. Then again, Mrs Josephine had also insisted on fresh cakes on the sideboard, a warm fire burning in the hearth, and a welcoming smile for visitors, but none of these greeted Lowri now.

She returned to the ridge, picked up her equipment, and walked away.

> Answer these questions about the text. You can refer back to the text if you need to.

1. Give another word or phrase that means the same as
   "fleeting" (line 5) as it is used in the text.

_____

2. Which of these words best describes the condition of the farmhouse? Tick the box next to the correct answer.

    A   decrepit   ☐

    B   unscathed   ☐

    C   obsolete   ☐

    D   anomalous   ☐

3. Explain why Lowri couldn't see the farmhouse properly at first.

_____

_____

4. "like a familiar face" (lines 6-7).
   What is this phrase an example of? Tick the box next to the correct answer.

    A   Onomatopoeia   ☐

    B   Personification   ☐

    C   A simile   ☐

    D   A proverb   ☐

5. How would you describe Lowri's colleague?
   Tick the box next to the correct answer.

    A   Adventurous   ☐

    B   Impatient   ☐

    C   Curious   ☐

    D   Negligent   ☐

TURN OVER ➡

6.   What has happened to the front wall?

_____

7.   According to the passage, which of these statements is false?
     Tick the box next to the correct answer.

     A   Lowri's colleague doesn't want to stop at the farmhouse.   ☐

     B   There aren't many other buildings nearby.   ☐

     C   It is already dark when they find the farmhouse.   ☐

     D   There is a field between the ridge and the farmhouse.   ☐

8.   "Mrs Josephine was a stickler for cleanliness." (Lines 15-16).
     Explain what this means in your own words.

_____

_____

9.   In your own words, explain how Lowri feels in lines 15-19.

_____

_____

END OF TEST

/ 9

Test 24: Proofreading

You have **10 minutes** to do this test. Work as quickly and accurately as you can.

> For each numbered line, choose the word, or group of words, which completes the passage correctly. The passage needs to make sense and be written in correct English. Circle the correct letter.

1. My aunts and uncles **our   haven't   are   aren't not   have** my parents' siblings.
       A   B   C   D   E

2. Next week, **they will   their   there   they'll   they're** all coming for Christmas,
       A   B   C   D   E

3. which is going to **bee   been   by   be   begin** busy. We are one chair short, so
       A   B   C   D   E

4. **whichever   whom   whoever is   whoever   who** arrives last has to sit on a stool.
       A   B   C   D   E

> This passage has some punctuation mistakes.
> Write the passage out again with the correct punctuation.

5. The three puppies — Ronald nancy and spot have just arrived at the pet shop the
    one behind the park)

_____

_____

_____

TURN OVER ➡

This passage contains some spelling mistakes. Each numbered line has either one mistake or no mistake. For each line, work out which group of words contains a mistake, and circle the correct letter. Circle N if there is no mistake.

6. The secret entrance to the spy headquarters was situated beneeth Mrs Wibble's

   A   B   C   D   N

7. bed of pink roses. One of the flowers contained a tiny fingerprinting devise,

   A   B   C   D   N

8. which authorised employees could use to gain acess to the department.

   A   B   C   D   N

9. Mrs Wibble had been a lifelong associate of this particular spy organisatian,

   A   B   C   D   N

10. though in recent years her ailing health had made it neccessary for her to retire

   A   B   C   D   N

11. gracefuly at the age of seventy-two. Her days of active service were remembered

    A   B   C   D   N

12. fondly by her colleagues, such as the time when she aprehended a villain using

    A   B   C   D   N

13. a deadly combination of a tea cosy, two knitting needles and a leather handbag.

    A   B   C   D   N

END OF TEST

/ 18

Time for a break! These puzzles will test your **synonym** and **word-making** skills.

Stepping Stones

Make your way down the river by finding the synonyms of 'happy'.

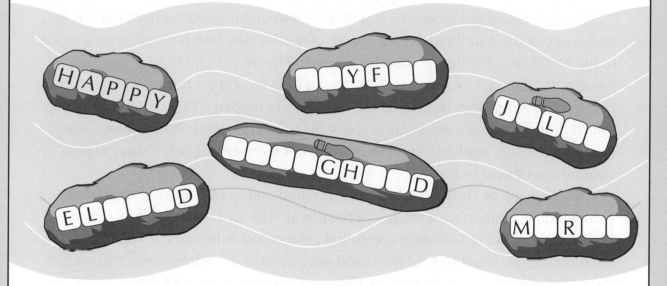

Word Chain

Place the groups of letters from the list into the boxes, so that each box makes
a word with the box that follows. Make sure you follow the direction of the
arrows. The first two have been done for you.

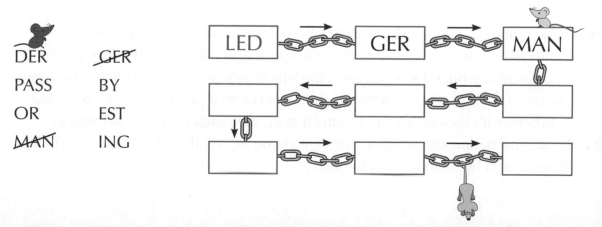

You have **10 minutes** to do this test. Work as quickly and accurately as you can.

Read this passage carefully and answer the questions that follow.

Holy Island

The Holy Island of Lindisfarne is a tranquil retreat, far removed from the hustle and bustle of the mainland, with a wealth of quiet sandy beaches and striking vistas of the North Sea. While the island is accessible by means of a road at low tide, twice a day the track is submerged as the sea rolls in, and for this reason, planning a
5   visit to Holy Island can require a little more effort compared to a visit to the average tourist destination. It is essential to check the tide timetable before visiting — the tidal refuge hut is available in times of need, but there are *far* better ways to pass your time on the island...

Climb the hill to Holy Island's castle. Perched on top of a rocky crag, it has a
10 commanding position over the rest of the island. The castle was built in 1550, following a period of turbulent events that culminated in Henry VIII's dissolution of the monasteries. Built to help the island resist Scottish invasion, rumour has it that the castle was constructed using stones from the monasteries' demise.

Visit the harbour. Once upon a time, Holy Island's harbour was an important hive
15 of industry for Northeasterners, who made a living from catching herrings, and later smoked them over wood fires. Nowadays, depending on the weather, the harbour can offer a site of peaceful contemplation one day, and by the next, present a scene of moody storms, whose waves crash dramatically over rocks and neighbouring islands.

20 Go nature spotting. Woolly bear caterpillars, big brown-lipped snails and common seals are just a selection of the species on offer. The area is well-known for its birdlife which descends upon the island over autumn and winter; in summer, carpets of dune flowers turn the sandy vastness into a picturesque sea of colour.

Whether it's the castle's fascinating history, the temperamental harbour or
25 the diverse nature and wildlife that entices you to visit the island, you won't be disappointed by all that it has to offer.

Answer these questions about the text. You can refer back to the text if you need to.

1. According to the text, how does the island differ from the mainland?

   _____

2. Give another word or phrase that means the same as "submerged" (line 4)
   as it is used in the text.

   _____

3. Why should tourists check the tide patterns before visiting the island?

   _____

4. What are the "times of need" (line 7) referring to in the text?
   Tick the box next to the correct answer.

   A   When tourists get lost on their way to the island   ☐

   B   Points during the day when there's a low tide   ☐

   C   Times when the sea has inundated the track to the mainland ☐

   D   Moments when swimmers require shelter   ☐

5. "a commanding position over the rest of the island" (lines 9-10).
   How does this description present the castle?

   _____

   _____

TURN OVER ➡

71   Test 25

6. Which of these words is closest in meaning to "turbulent" (line 11)?
   Tick the box next to the correct answer.

   A Surprising ☐

   B Chaotic ☐

   C Captivating ☐

   D Incessant ☐

7. How did Northeasterners earn money at the harbour in the past?

   _____

   _____

8. "The area is well-known for its birdlife which descends upon the island over **autumn** and **winter**" (lines 21-22). What are the words in bold examples of?
   Tick the box next to the correct answer.

   A Proper nouns ☐

   B Collective nouns ☐

   C Abstract nouns ☐

   D Pronouns ☐

9. Why is the harbour described as "temperamental" (line 24)?

   _____

   _____

END OF TEST

/ 9

You have **10 minutes** to do this test. Work as quickly and accurately as you can.

For each numbered line, choose the word, or group of words, which completes the passage correctly. The passage needs to make sense and be written in correct English. Circle the correct letter.

1. Paella is a popular dish **serving   serves   served   serve   severed** in most Spanish
    A   B   C   D   E

2. restaurants. It's **a   the   these   an   this** rice-based meal which may contain
    A   B   C   D   E

3. a mixture **with   of   to   consisting   for** chicken, prawns, mussels or vegetables.
    A   B   C   D   E

4. **Theirs   There are   There're   There's   They're** one ingredient, however, that should
    A   B   C   D   E

5. not be forgotten — saffron, **who   what   which   that   where** is a food colouring
    A   B   C   D   E

6. that **turned   has turned   had turned   will have turned   turns** the rice bright
    A   B   C   D   E

7. yellow. **Traditionally   Traditional   Tradition   Traditionary   Traditionless** ,
    A   B   C   D   E

8. paella **is cooking   is cooked   will be cooked   were cooked   are cooked**
    A   B   C   D   E

outside, on a wood fire, in a special paella pan.

TURN OVER ➡

73   Test 26

9. Contrery to popular belief, a goldfish's memory spans beyond three seconds, and sceintists believe they can recall infermation for up to five months, so the general concensus is that fish aren't that forgetfull after all.

_____

_____

_____

_____

10. During the second round the first dancing duo tom and June — will perform the tango This will be the twenty first time that they've danced together.

_____

_____

_____

END OF TEST

/ 18

Test 27: Comprehension

You have **10 minutes** to do this test. Work as quickly and accurately as you can.

Read this passage carefully and answer the questions that follow.

An extract from 'The Raven'

Once upon a midnight dreary, while I pondered, weak and weary,
Over many a quaint and curious volume of forgotten lore*,
While I nodded, nearly napping, suddenly there came a tapping,
As of some one gently rapping, rapping at my chamber door.
5   "'T is some visitor," I muttered, "tapping at my chamber door—
Only this, and nothing more."

Ah, distinctly I remember it was in the bleak December,
And each separate dying ember wrought its ghost upon the floor.
Eagerly I wished the morrow:—vainly I had sought to borrow
10   From my books surcease* of sorrow—sorrow for the lost Lenore—
For the rare and radiant maiden whom the angels name Lenore—
Nameless here for evermore.

And the silken sad uncertain rustling of each purple curtain
Thrilled me—filled me with fantastic terrors never felt before;
15   So that now, to still the beating of my heart, I stood repeating
"'T is some visitor entreating entrance at my chamber door
Some late visitor entreating entrance at my chamber door;—
This it is, and nothing more."

Presently my soul grew stronger; hesitating then no longer,
20   "Sir," said I, "or Madam, truly your forgiveness I implore;
But the fact is I was napping, and so gently you came rapping,
And so faintly you came tapping, tapping at my chamber door,
That I scarce was sure I heard yous—here I opened wide the door;—
Darkness there, and nothing more.

Edgar Allan Poe

* lore — *stories*; * surcease — *relief*

TURN OVER ➡

1. Where is the narrator when he hears a tapping noise?

   _____

2. The fire is about to go out. What information in the poem tells you this?

   _____

   _____

3. What does the narrator do to stop himself feeling sad?
   Tick the box next to the correct answer.

   A   He waits for the next day.   ☐

   B   He thinks of Lenore.   ☐

   C   He reads something.   ☐

   D   He relights the fire.   ☐

4. What effect does the noise of the curtains' movement have on the narrator?

   _____

5. In your own words, explain how the narrator tries to calm himself.

   _____

   _____

6. "hesitating then no longer" (line 19). What type of word is 'longer' as it is used in this phrase? Tick the box next to the correct answer.

   A   Adverb   ☐

   B   Adjective   ☐

   C   Noun   ☐

   D   Verb   ☐

7. Give another word or phrase that means the same as "implore" (line 20) as it is used in the text.

   _____

8. "And so faintly you came tapping, tapping at my chamber door" (line 22). Which literary device is used in this line? Tick the box next to the correct answer.

   A   A simile   ☐

   B   Rhyme   ☐

   C   Onomatopoeia   ☐

   D   A metaphor   ☐

9. The narrator thinks that the tapping is only a visitor. How do you know that this isn't true?

   _____

   _____

END OF TEST

/ 9

Puzzles 9

No doubt you're ready for a couple of puzzles to exercise your **word-meaning** skills.

Word Family Frolics

Five words are hidden in the grid. Each word belongs to the same word family as one of the words below. Circle the words, but make sure you find the correct word type.

Example: Find a noun related to 'skilful'.

a) Find a noun related to 'quick'.

b) Find an adjective related to 'strangely'.

c) Find an adverb related to 'intelligence'.

d) Find a verb related to 'runner'.

e) Find a verb related to 'courier'.

R	D	U	T	H	F	D	C
E	E	N	A	Y	P	E	L
L	E	W	B	X	O	L	E
C	P	E	I	A	D	I	V
H	S	I	L	J	Z	V	E
S	P	R	I	N	T	E	R
A	O	D	T	B	S	R	L
K	G	E	Y	V	Y	I	Y

Double Trouble

Solve the clues below to find three words that mean something different when they are spelled backwards.

a) Forwards I come after main courses. Backwards I am anxious.

—————————

b) Forwards I exist. Backwards I am wicked.

————

c) Forwards I am a celebrity. Backwards I am some rodents.

————

You have **10 minutes** to do this test. Work as quickly and accurately as you can.

This passage contains some punctuation mistakes. Each numbered line has either one mistake or no mistake. For each line, work out which group of words contains a mistake, and circle the correct letter. Circle N if there is no mistake.

1. We're moving house tomorrow, so I can't get to any of my things — they're all

    A　　**B**　　**C**　　**D**　　**N**

2. packed into boxes. Luxmi, my older sister is upset about moving because we're

    A　　**B**　　**C**　　**D**　　**N**

3. going to a village. "You're basically moving me to outer space" she said. My

    A　　**B**　　**C**　　**D**　　**N**

4. mum called this "a dramatic overreaction" because its only two miles away.

    A　　**B**　　**C**　　**D**　　**N**

5. I agree with mum. The village sounds far better: there's loads of outdoor space

    A　　**B**　　**C**　　**D**　　**N**

6. (a vast improvement on the tiny paved garden we've got at the moment) the

    A　　**B**　　**C**　　**D**　　**N**

7. main street has a sweet shop and; my new room's bigger, which is the best thing.

    A　　**B**　　**C**　　**D**　　**N**

8. Luxmi's always focusing on negatives; I'm an optimist, and I can't wait.

    A　　**B**　　**C**　　**D**　　**N**

TURN OVER ➡

For each numbered line, choose the word, or group of words, which completes the passage correctly. The passage needs to make sense and be written in correct English. Circle the correct letter.

9. Liam has an obsession **of from with to in** insects. He keeps stick insects
                          A   B   C   D E

10. in a tank in **her these them his me** bedroom. Liam's mum is the opposite
              A   B   C   D   E

11. — she hates bugs. **In case Indeed Despite Although Yet** this, Liam wants
                 A   B   C   D   E

12. to buy a more **big bigger large spacious larger** tank to hold new species.
              A   B   C   D   E

This passage contains some spelling mistakes.
Write the passage out again with the correct spellings.

13. We're doing a class art progect in mixed media. Our teacher says we all have to
    make a contrabution, weather we choose paint, collarge or sculpture. We've split
    it into eight seperate sections, so their's lots of variety.

_____

_____

_____

_____

END OF TEST

/ 18

You have **10 minutes** to do this test. Work as quickly and accurately as you can.

For each numbered line, choose the word, or group of words, which completes the passage correctly. The passage needs to make sense and be written in correct English. Circle the correct letter.

1. To make the cake, first **beats beat beet beated beating** the sugar and
                       A   **B**   **C**   **D**   **E**

2. butter in a large bowl **if unless other with until** light and fluffy. Then,
                       A   **B**   **C**   **D**   **E**

3. **taking take takeing took takes** care not to get any shell in the mix, add two
      A   **B**   **C**   **D**   **E**

4. eggs. Next, gently fold in the flour **and at an a the** spoon at a time.
                       A **B** **C** **D** **E**

This passage has some punctuation mistakes.
Write the passage out again with the correct punctuation.

5. were going to Rajs birthday party tomorrow which includes rugby, tag a birthday tea
    a film and a sleepover

    _____

    _____

    _____

TURN OVER ➡

This passage contains some spelling mistakes. Each numbered line has either one mistake or no mistake. For each line, work out which group of words contains a mistake, and circle the correct letter. Circle N if there is no mistake.

6. The Venus flytrap is a carnivorous plant nateive to a small region of the United
        A   B   C   D   N

7. States of America, though it has also been introduced elsewear. The plant traps
        A   B   C   D   N

8. its pray between two leaf surfaces, which are hinged together, like a piece of
        A   B   C   D   N

9. paper folded in half. The trapping mechanism is triggerred by contact with a
        A   B   C   D   N

10. hair — there are usually two to five hairs destributed on each leaf surface
        A   B   C   D   N

11. — causing the two halves to snap shut and imprison the insect. Once the insect
        A   B   C   D   N

12. has been digested, the two halves reopen in preperation for another victim. The
        A   B   C   D   N

13. plant's surfaces are coated in a thick, gluey protien, designed to entice insects in.
        A   B   C   D   N

END OF TEST

/ 18

You have **10 minutes** to do this test. Work as quickly and accurately as you can.

> Read this passage carefully and answer the questions that follow.

Hot air balloons

In 1782, a Frenchman named Joseph Montgolfier was sitting beside the fire. He watched the fragments of embers rising slowly up the chimney and witnessing the sparks being lifted by a force gave him an idea.

5   He set to work on a model, stretching a piece of lightweight fabric over a thin wooden frame and resting it on a support. When he ignited some paper beneath the structure, it rose into the air and hit the ceiling — the lighter, hot air could lift objects through the colder, surrounding air. Joseph quickly wrote to his younger brother, Étienne, promising to show him "one of the most astonishing sights in the world".

10   The Montgolfier brothers went on to build the first hot air balloon to carry human cargo and launched it from the centre of Paris on 21st November 1783. The first flight to carry live passengers had taken place on 19th September the same year, transporting a sheep, a duck and a rooster for two miles. This new balloon surpassed that, flying for twenty-five minutes and covering five and a

15 half miles. Apparently, when the balloon landed in nearby fields, its pilots gave champagne to the shocked farmers to reassure them that they weren't demons that had come down from the sky. This, however, is often regarded as legend.

Hot air ballooning suddenly became fashionable. Designers started using hydrogen — a lighter gas — instead of hot air, allowing for longer flights. By the

20 end of 1785, men had flown across the English Channel in a balloon. Today, people have even circumnavigated the globe.

TURN OVER ➡

Answer these questions about the text. You can refer back to the text if you need to.

1.   How did Joseph get the inspiration for his hot air balloon?

   _____

2.   Why does hot air make a balloon float?
     Tick the box next to the correct answer.

     A   Because it's lighter than a balloon.   ☐

     B   Because it's heavier than hydrogen.   ☐

     C   Because it can be set alight.   ☐

     D   Because it's lighter than cold air.   ☐

3.   How did Joseph feel when his first model worked?
     Tick the box next to the correct answer.

     A   Apprehensive   ☐

     B   Incredulous   ☐

     C   Captivated   ☐

     D   Troubled   ☐

4.   What happened after the brothers launched their balloon in Paris?
     Tick the box next to the correct answer.

     A   They decided they would try transporting animals.   ☐

     B   Their balloon stayed in the air for twenty-five minutes.   ☐

     C   They made a model out of fabric and wood.   ☐

     D   Their balloon flew across the English Channel.   ☐

5. "This, however, is often regarded as legend." (Line 17).
Explain what this sentence means in your own words.

_____

_____

6. "Hot air ballooning suddenly became fashionable." (Line 18).
What type of word is "suddenly" as it is used in this sentence?

_____

7. In what way were later hot air balloons different from Joseph's original design?

_____

_____

8. Which of these statements is false?
Tick the box next to the correct answer.

   A   Joseph was older than Étienne.   ☐

   B   The first hot air balloon flight took place in November 1783.   ☐

   C   Farmers shocked by the hot air balloons were appeased.   ☐

   D   Joseph's initial balloon model made him optimistic.   ☐

9. Which of these phrases is closest in meaning to "circumnavigated" (line 21)?
Tick the box next to the correct answer.

   A   Travelled around   ☐

   B   Quickly surrounded   ☐

   C   Circled under   ☐

   D   Mapped through   ☐

END OF TEST

/ 9

Time for a break! These puzzles are a great way to practise your **spelling** skills.

Repair It

Each of the words below has one spelling mistake. Circle the incorrect letter in each word, and write the correct letter into the numbered box. The correct letters give the answer to the joke!

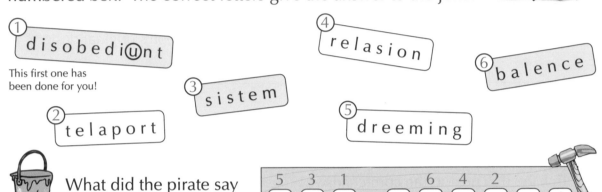

① d i s o b e d i (u) n t

This first one has been done for you!

② t e l a p o r t

③ s i s t e m

④ r e l a s i o n

⑤ d r e e m i n g

⑥ b a l e n c e

What did the pirate say on his eightieth birthday?

5	3	1		6	4	2	
		e	m				y	!

Cube Words

Using just the letters in the cube, can you spell the answers to the clues? You can only use each letter once in each word.

P	C	L
S	E	A
N	A	D

Every answer must use the letter 'E'.

a verb meaning 'move to music' ....

another word for 'location' ....

something you light with a match ....

you often find these in shoes ....

Can you find the nine letter word? _ _ _ _ _ _ _ _ _

Hint: it's another word for 'scenery'.

You have **10 minutes** to do this test. Work as quickly and as accurately as you can.

> This passage contains some spelling mistakes.
> Write the passage out again with the correct spellings.

1. It was a gloomey day; the wind was blusterring loudly against the windows. The rain fell ralentlessly threwout the day, so many atempted to protect themselfs with spindly umbrellas.

    _____

    _____

    _____

    _____

> This passage has some punctuation mistakes.
> Write the passage out again with the correct punctuation.

2. "What a day! sighed Sarah throwing her bag onto the living room armchair. she collapsed, exhausted onto the couch, closing her eyes immediately.

    _____

    _____

    _____

TURN OVER

Test 31

For each numbered line, choose the word, or group of words, which completes the passage correctly. The passage needs to make sense and be written in correct English. Circle the correct letter.

3. This weekend, I am **going to** **going** **go** **went** **about to** camping with my
                    A   B   C   D   E

4. parents. I hope the weather is nice so we don't **have** **need** **have to** **go to** **leave**
                       A   B   C   D   E

5. stay inside all day. If it is warm, then we **would** **could** **shouldn't** **will** **can** be
                   A   B   C   D   E

6. able to go out for walks and **go** **has** **be** **should** **have** picnics. I suppose I
                   A   B   C   D   E

7. wouldn't mind if it **rained** **would** **raining** **did** **rain** a tiny bit, as long as it wasn't
              A   B   C   D   E

8. too heavy. In fact, it's sometimes quite refreshing **while** **at** **on** **if** **whether** it
                      A   B   C   D   E

9. starts raining when **you're** **your** **you** **it's** **they** on a long walk in hot weather!
                A   B   C   D   E

10. I'm sure the weather won't stop us **for** **from** **having** **going** **with** fun anyway.
                A   B   C   D   E

END OF TEST

/ 18

You have **10 minutes** to do this test. Work as quickly and as accurately as you can.

Read this passage carefully and answer the questions that follow.

Adapted from 'Black Beauty'

One day a shabby, miserable-looking driver, who went by the name of 'Seedy Sam', brought in his horse looking dreadfully beat, and the Governor said:

"You and your horse look more fit for the police station than for this rank."

The man flung his tattered rug over the horse, turned full round upon the Governor
5 and said in a voice that sounded almost desperate:

"If the police have any business with the matter it ought to be with the masters who charge us so much, or with the fares that are fixed so low. If a man has to pay eighteen shillings a day for the use of a cab and two horses, as many of us have to do in the season, and must make that up before we earn a penny for ourselves I say 'tis
10 more than hard work; nine shillings a day to get out of each horse before you begin to get your own living. You know that's true, and if the horses don't work we must starve, and I and my children have known what that is before now. I've six of 'em, and only one earns anything; I am on the stand fourteen or sixteen hours a day, and I haven't had a Sunday these ten or twelve weeks; you know Skinner never gives a day
15 if he can help it, and if I don't work hard, tell me who does! I want a warm coat and a mackintosh, but with so many to feed how can a man get it? I had to pledge my clock a week ago to pay Skinner, and I shall never see it again."

Anna Sewell

Answer these questions about the text. You can refer back to the text if you need to.

1. Give another word or phrase that means the same as
   "beat" (line 2) as it is used in the text.

TURN OVER ➡

2. What is Seedy Sam's occupation?

_____

3. Which of these words best describes how the Governor thinks Seedy Sam looks?
   Tick the box next to the correct answer.

   A   Competent   ☐

   B   Guilty   ☐

   C   Exhausted   ☐

   D   Disreputable   ☐

4. According to the text, why doesn't Seedy Sam charge more for his fares?

_____

5. How much money must Seedy Sam earn before he makes any profit?
   Tick the box next to the correct answer.

   A   A penny   ☐

   B   9 shillings   ☐

   C   18 shillings   ☐

   D   27 shillings   ☐

6. "You know that's true, and if the horses don't work we must starve, and
    I and my children have known what that is before now." (Lines 11-12).
    Which of these words is an adjective? Tick the box next to the correct answer.

    A   before   ☐

    B   must   ☐

    C   starve   ☐

    D   true   ☐

7. How many of Seedy Sam's children don't contribute financially to the family?

    _____

8. Which of these is not a reason why Seedy Sam is poor?
    Tick the box next to the correct answer.

    A   It's expensive to rent horses.   ☐

    B   It's expensive to rent carriages.   ☐

    C   He has a large family to feed.   ☐

    D   He doesn't get enough business.   ☐

9. Which of the following words best describes Skinner?
    Tick the box next to the correct answer.

    A   Sympathetic   ☐

    B   Unforgiving   ☐

    C   Hard-working   ☐

    D   Generous   ☐

END OF TEST

/ 9

You have **10 minutes** to do this test. Work as quickly and as accurately as you can.

> Read this passage carefully and answer the questions that follow.

Northern Lights

It's night. You're standing outside, waiting, eyes straining towards the horizon. All of a sudden, you think you see something — a faint yellow-green glow in the distance. Eventually, this light grows stronger and arches over the sky, forming giant curtains that flutter and wave as though in front of an open window. There are lots of colours now:

5 turquoise, blue and violet. What you've just seen is a phenomenon that many people make their mission to see: the Northern Lights.

This remarkable natural light show, also known as the aurora borealis, occurs above the North Pole when particles from the sun make contact with gases in the Earth's atmosphere. Alaska, Iceland and Norway are among the best places to spot

10 the Northern Lights, however precise sightings are notoriously difficult to predict. Scientists are especially keen to remedy this because these light shows have been known to cause power blackouts.

The lights can occur at any time (but note that they aren't visible to the naked eye during the day), though they are at their most frequent and spectacular every eleven

15 years. Faint displays of the lights can often be seen in Scotland, but when they're at their peak, the lights can often be seen further south in Britain. So next time there are reported sightings in Britain, take some time to stand outside and stare at the night sky. If you manage to catch a clear and cloudless night, in a location with low light pollution and a good view of the horizon, you just might witness one of the most

20 sought-after sights in the world.

> Answer these questions about the text. You can refer back to the text if you need to.

1. Find a phrase from the text that contains a metaphor.

_____

2. "Eventually, this light grows stronger and arches over the sky, forming giant curtains that flutter and wave as though in front of an open window." (Lines 3-4).
Which of these words is an adverb? Tick the box next to the correct answer.

A   stronger ☐

B   grows ☐

C   flutter ☐

D   Eventually ☐

3. Give another word or phrase that means the same as "phenomenon" (line 5) as it is used in the text.

_____

4. Why is the phenomenon known as the "Northern Lights"?
Tick the box next to the correct answer.

A   It can only be seen in locations north of Britain. ☐

B   It can only be seen from the North Pole. ☐

C   It takes place above the North Pole. ☐

D   It is best viewed when looking north. ☐

5. Which of the words below is closest in meaning to the word "notoriously" (line 10)?
Tick the box next to the correct answer.

A   Relatively ☐

B   Consistently ☐

C   Undoubtedly ☐

D   Infamously ☐

TURN OVER ➡

6. Why can it be difficult to see the Northern Lights?
   Tick the box next to the correct answer.

   A   It takes a lot of effort to find them. ☐

   B   They are only seen once every 11 years. ☐

   C   It is never known exactly when they will occur. ☐

   D   It is difficult to find a location to view them from. ☐

7. In what way can the Northern Lights disrupt everyday life?

   _____

   _____

8. Why are the lights best viewed at night? Tick the box next to the correct answer.

   A   The places they are visible from have more hours of darkness. ☐

   B   They cannot be seen when it is light. ☐

   C   The phenomenon does not happen during the day. ☐

   D   They occur more frequently at night. ☐

9. In your own words, explain what the phrase "one of the most sought-after sights" (lines 19-20) means.

   _____

   _____

END OF TEST

/ 9

E6XPE1

CGP

11+
English

Ages
10-11

The
Answer Book

Book 1

English

D0550055

Practise • Prepare • Pass
Everything your child needs for 11+ success

E6XPE1

Test 1 — pages 2-4

1. The Eiffel Tower is a distinctive feature that stands out above the city of Paris.
"characterises" means that something stands out as a prominent feature, so if it "characterises the Paris skyline", it means that it is a distinctive feature of the city's outline against the sky.

2. "Like a giraffe stretching for the leaves from the highest trees"
This phrase on lines 2-3 compares the Eiffel Tower to a giraffe to emphasise its height. It uses the word "like", so it must be a simile.

3. various answers possible
E.g. 'condemned' means the same as 'disapproved of' or 'declared unfit'.

4. D
Lines 8-9 state that some people felt the tower "would detract significantly from the traditional beauty of Paris's other famous monuments".

5. B
'Confident' describes Gustave Eiffel, therefore it is an adjective.

6. C
Lines 15-16 state "as Eiffel had predicted, the exhibition was a hit".

7. A
The Eiffel Tower is not really a giant, but, like a giant, it is very big.

8. sending communications
A 'secondary purpose' means 'another purpose', and line 21 states that "Paris officials decided that the tower served as an effective communications tower".

9. Plans to remove the tower after it had been in place for twenty years were abandoned.
Lines 22-23 state "In 1910, the tower was granted a reprieve". A reprieve is the cancellation or postponement of something.

Test 2 — pages 5-6

1. To help me remember Ian's birthday, I put a note on my calendar in big, bold letters. I forgot about it last year, and it was very embarrassing. He looked so disappointed when I next saw him, and I felt terrible.
The bits that are underlined show where a spelling mistake has been corrected. You get one mark for each of the following words you have spelt correctly: 'remember', 'calendar', 'embarrassing', 'disappointed' and 'terrible'.

2. The waiter looked at Fred. "He'll have a fruit salad," said his sister. Fred scowled, and looked longingly at a piece of cake, but he didn't say anything.
The bits that are underlined show where punctuation has been corrected. You get one mark for each of the following: a capital letter at the start of 'The'; speech marks before 'He'll'; an apostrophe in 'He'll'; a comma after 'cake'; and a full stop after 'anything'.

3. C
'that' is correct because it refers back to 'chocolate'.

4. E
'but' is the conjunction that makes the most sense.

5. A
'don't' is correct because it agrees with the noun 'people' and is in the correct tense.

6. D
'they're' is correct because 'they' is the plural pronoun that refers to the cocoa beans. 'they're' is a contraction of 'they are' — 'are' agrees with 'they' and is in the correct tense.

7. B
'are' is correct because it agrees with the plural noun 'beans' and is in the correct tense.

8. E
'as' is correct because it completes the phrase 'known as'.

9. A
'its' is correct because it refers back to the paste.

10. B
'with' makes the most sense in this sentence because it completes the phrase 'enhanced with' — none of the other options fit the phrase.

Test 3 — pages 7-9

1. C
Lines 2-3 state that Harry received an education at one of those institutions after he had attended private school, and they go on to state that he "had received the ordinary education of a gentleman". Therefore, the answer must be 'universities'.

2. His only parent was weak and ignorant, meaning he could do what he pleased.
Lines 4-6 state "his only surviving parent being both weak and ignorant, he was permitted thenceforward to spend his time in the attainment of petty and purely elegant accomplishments".

3. Harry was neither good at sport nor activities requiring hard work.
"For all active and industrious pursuits" is another way of saying "physical activities and tasks that require hard work", so if Harry was unfitted by nature and training, it means that he naturally wasn't very good at them, and he didn't try to work hard at them.

4.   D

Harry does not literally have a dove's eyes — the author is comparing his eyes to a dove's to suggest that Harry has small and kind eyes — so this must be a metaphor.

5.   A

'Submissive' and 'compliant' both mean 'obedient'.

6.   B

Line 15 states "A fortunate chance and some influence" got Harry the job of private secretary.

7.   various answers possible

E.g. 'boisterous' means the same as 'lively' or 'energetic'.

8.   Sir Thomas appears to be the opposite of Harry. Sir Thomas is domineering, whereas Harry is submissive.

Lines 12-13 state that Harry "had an air of agreeable tenderness and melancholy and the most submissive and caressing manners". Lines 17-18 state "Sir Thomas was a man of sixty, loud-spoken, boisterous, and domineering".

9.   "had been often whispered and repeatedly denied"

Whispering about something and denying information are indicators that something is being kept a secret.

Puzzles 1 — page 10

Inspector English's Investigation

various answers possible

E.g.   They **aren't** near any water.

I **haven't** hidden them in a building.

I hid them somewhere **which** (OR **that**) is high up.

I **put** them near a bird's nest.

*The goods are hidden **in the tree** — this is the only place that isn't near any water and isn't a building, and is somewhere high up that is near a bird's nest.*

Test 4 — pages 11-12

1.   B

'Whose' is correct because it shows possession. The advice belongs to Lianne.

2.   C

'have' is correct because it completes the phrase 'I should have'.

3.   A

'had been' is correct because it is in the pluperfect tense, so it refers to a time frame further in the past than 'She reminded me'.

4.   B

'ought' is correct because it is the only modal verb in the list that can be followed by 'to'.

5.   Kerry ach<u>ie</u>ved an excellent mark in her spelling test. She found the beginn<u>in</u>g of the test challeng<u>in</u>g, but since she had practi<u>s</u>ed the words beforehand, she remained confid<u>en</u>t that she would be successful.

The bits that are underlined show where a spelling mistake has been corrected. You get one mark for each of the following words you have spelt correctly: 'achieved', 'beginning', 'challenging', 'practised', 'confident' and 'successful'.

6.   D

There should be an apostrophe at the end of 'teachers' (teachers'). The apostrophe shows possession — the Christmas party belongs to the teachers.

7.   B

'whos' should be 'who's' — there needs to be an apostrophe before the 's' to show that 'who's' is a contraction of 'who is'.

8.   N

There are no mistakes in this line.

9.   A

There should be a comma between 'food' and 'everyone' to separate the fronted adverbial from the following sentence.

10.   A

There should be speech marks in front of 'I'm' to show that someone has started to speak.

11.   B

'Its' should be 'It's' — there needs to be an apostrophe before the 's' to show that 'It's' is a contraction of 'It is'.

12.   N

There are no mistakes in this line.

13.   D

There should be a full stop after 'canteen' to mark the end of the sentence.

Test 5 — pages 13-15

1.   various answers possible

You get one mark for any one of the following explanations: this house is "lonely" and is not located on the road, which means the burglars are unlikely to be seen; OR its windows are low, which means entering the house should be quite easy; OR its inhabitants have "Old-fashioned eyes" which indicates that elderly people live there, and they are an easier target for burglars.

2.   The occupants are old.

"Old-fashioned eyes" suggests that the occupants are elderly.

3.   D

'Gag' and 'silence' both mean 'to prevent something from making a sound'.

4.   **a tense atmosphere that shows the burglars are nervous about being caught**

Lines 19-23 suggest that the burglars are paranoid — they think that inanimate objects like the pair of glasses, the almanac, the mat and the moon are aware of what they're doing, and have come to disrupt them and to "see who's there" (line 24).

5.   C

Nervousness is a human emotion, so describing a star as nervous is an example of personification.

6.   B

Line 25 refers to the tankard, the spoon, the brooch and the stone as "plunder", which means 'property that is about to be acquired illegally'.

7.   various answers possible

E.g. 'stealth' means the same as 'slyness' or 'secrecy'.

8.   It's getting light, and the burglars are running out of time to flee the house before everyone wakes up.

Given that the sun moves across the sky throughout the day, the fact that "The sun has got as far / As the third sycamore" suggests that it's been light for a while, and the burglars are running out of time to flee the house before anyone wakes up and catches them.

9.   C

Line 40 states that the door has been left "ajar", which is another word for 'open'.

Test 6 — pages 16-18

1.   B

Line 1 states "Alfred Wainwright has delighted, informed and inspired fellwalkers for decades" — 'fellwalkers' is another word for 'ramblers' or 'people who enjoy rambling'.

2.   C

'Humble' means 'modest'. Wainwright's family is not described as destitute (or poor), nor is his family described as privileged (or wealthy). There is also no mention of abuse.

3.   D

Lines 7 and 8 state "He attended night school and gained qualifications which provided him with opportunities to advance".

4.   A

'Stark' and 'complete' both mean 'absolute'.

5.   a trip to the Lake District

A catalyst is something that causes something else to happen. Line 12 states "This trip started his life-long passion for the Lake District".

6.   various answers possible

E.g. 'intimately' means the same as 'familiarly' or 'personally'.

7.   Wainwright was very passionate about the Lake District, so dedicating so much time to making the guides demonstrated his love for the fells, just like a love letter.

A love letter allows someone to demonstrate their love for someone or something. In making the pictorial guides to the Lake District, Wainwright was able to show his passion and enthusiasm for the Lakeland fells.

8.   D

'Incredibly' is an adverb because it is describing the adjectives 'accurate' and 'detailed'.

9.   various answers possible

You get one mark for any of the following explanations: the fact that many people aim to climb the fells shows that they are popular; OR the word "challenge" shows they must be difficult to climb; OR the phrase "over their lifetime" suggests that the challenge is not easy, and therefore it can take a long time to climb them all.

Puzzles 2 — page 19

Word Connections

doorway — **entrance** — bewitch

shrink — **contract** — agreement

waste — **refuse** — reject

injury — **wound** — wrapped

Punctuation Pandemonium

I love cooking, my family and my cat.

Cooking can be a verb or a noun. Without the comma, "cooking" could be interpreted as a verb, so the sentence would suggest that Eric likes cooking his family and his cat.

I think it's time to eat, Dad.

The comma introduces the person the statement is addressed to. Without the comma, Eric admits he eats his dad.

Test 7 — pages 20-21

1.   D

'when' is correct because it is being used as a synonym of 'during' in this context.

2.   C

'of' is correct because it completes the phrase 'the freedom of'.

3.   E

'have' is correct because it is a verb in the correct tense that completes the phrase 'have an accident'.

4.   B

'should' is correct because it is a modal verb that introduces advice about wearing a helmet correctly.

5. **"Look, there it is,"** said Ashleigh, pointing at the long grass. **//** **"You've found it,"** I shouted in excitement, running over to where she was standing.

The bits that are underlined show where punctuation has been corrected. You get one mark for each of the following: speech marks before 'Look'; a comma after 'is' (an exclamation mark is also acceptable after 'is'); a full stop after 'grass'; a new paragraph after "grass."; speech marks before 'You've'; and a comma after 'excitement'.

6. **A**
'brilliant' should be 'brilliant' — the ending is 'ant'.

7. **B**
'beutiful' should be 'beautiful'.

8. **C**
'caneoing' should be 'canoeing' — the root word is 'canoe'.

9. **N**
There are no mistakes in this line.

10. **C**
'musuem' should be 'museum'.

11. **A**
'apparantly' should be 'apparently' — the root word is 'apparent'.

12. **A**
'restaraunt' should be 'restaurant'.

13. **D**
'behavour' should be 'behaviour' — the ending is 'iour'.

Test 8 — pages 22-24

1. **various answers possible**
E.g. 'roused' means the same as 'woke' or 'stirred'.

2. **so she has more light to be able to read them properly**
Line 4 states that the light in the bedroom is dim. It is likely, therefore, that Clover unhooks the rules and takes them to the window where the light would be brighter, so she can read them properly.

3. **C**
The girls get up at 6 o'clock and have half an hour to get ready. Therefore, they have to be ready by 6:30 am.

4. **private prayer**
"silent devotion" is another way of saying 'prayer'. The fact that it is 'silent' suggests that it is private prayer.

5. **C**
Line 11 states "It is never easy to be quick, when one is in a hurry".

6. **A**
Line 13 states "Katy and Clover were barely ready when the second bell sounded", suggesting that the girls should have been ready by the time the second bell sounded. Line 14 says that they "hastened downstairs", indicating that the purpose of the second bell was to prompt them to go downstairs.

7. **hastened**
'Hurried' and 'hastened' both mean 'rushed'.

8. **B**
Lines 7-10 indicate that Clover doesn't like to break the rules, as she makes a special effort to read the rules hanging in their room. After reading the rules, it obvious from her haste that she is panicking about how much she has to do in the time allowed, and the consequences of not getting everything done in that time.

9. **C**
'for' is a preposition.

Test 9 — pages 25-26

1. **The weather forecast for tomorrow has predicted severe snow for much of the country. It is recommended that only essential journeys are made because the roads are likely to be treacherous.**

The bits that are underlined show where a spelling mistake has been corrected. You get one mark for each of the following words you have spelt correctly: 'forecast', 'tomorrow', 'recommended', 'essential', 'journeys' and 'treacherous'.

2. **Despite the road closure, it's still possible to go out. Put on some suitable shoes (such as walking boots), leave in good time, and walk rather than drive.**

The bits that are underlined show where punctuation has been corrected. You got one mark for each of the following: a comma after 'closure'; an apostrophe in 'it's'; a bracket after 'boots'; and a full stop after 'drive'.

3. **B**
'are' is correct because it agrees with the plural noun 'Dachshunds', and it is in the correct tense.

4. **E**
'they' is correct because it refers to 'Dachshunds'.

5. **B**
'Their' is correct because it is a plural possessive adjective that agrees with 'Dachshunds'.

6. **D**
'for' is correct because it introduces the Dachshund's original purpose and completes the phrase 'for hunting'.

7. **A**
'has' is correct because it is in the correct tense and agrees with the singular subject — 'their distinctive shape'.

8. **C**
'show' is correct because it agrees with the plural noun 'dogs', and it is in the correct tense.

9. **C**
'However' is correct because it signposts a counterargument.

10. **D**
'which' is correct because it introduces the relative clause that follows.

Puzzles 3 — page 27

Crossword Contest

Odd One Out

Hidden word: *irritated*

'Indignant' is the odd one out because all the other words mean 'afraid', whereas 'indignant' means 'angry'. 'Irritated' is a synonym for 'angry'.

Test 10 — pages 28-29

1.   D
'took' is correct because it is in the past tense, which makes it consistent with the next sentence.

2.   C
'wasn't' is correct because it is in the correct tense and it agrees with the subject 'I'.

3.   A
'standing' makes the most sense in this sentence because it describes what they were doing on the terraces.

4.   C
'will have' is correct as it is indicating the likelihood that the narrator will attend a football match in the future.

5.   Having recently been ref<u>u</u>rbished, 'Joy's Food Emporium' is now open again for bus<u>i</u>ness. Refreshm<u>e</u>nts are availabl<u>e</u> as usual, including our fa<u>m</u>ous pints of tea, as well as some delic<u>i</u>ous new creations.
The bits that are underlined show where a spelling mistake has been corrected. You get one mark for each of the following words you have spelt correctly: 'refurbished', 'business', 'Refreshments', 'available', 'famous' and 'delicious'.

6.   N
There are no mistakes in this line.

7.   B
'unexplained-knitting' does not need a hyphen — it should be replaced with a space.

8.   C
There should be a comma after 'lampposts' to separate the items in the list.

9.   A
There should not be a comma after 'themselves'.

10.   D
There should be a capital letter at the start of 'it's' because this is the first word that is spoken.

11.   A
There should be speech marks after the full stop because this is the end of the speech.

12.   B
There should not be a semicolon after 'cosies'.

13.   C
There should not be an apostrophe in 'it's' because it shows that the inhabitants belong to Woollerton. 'It's' cannot be replaced with 'it is' or 'it has' in this sentence, so it has to be written as 'its'.

Test 11 — pages 30-32

1.   various answers possible
You get one mark for either of the following answers: guns become warm when they have been firing for a long time — line 3 states that the guns are heated; OR the word "weary" on line 4 suggests that the guns are tired, therefore they must have been firing for a long time.

2.   B
In the phrase "silent scoff", both words begin with 's', therefore this phrase is an example of alliteration.

3.   Britain
Lines 17-18 state that the brave hearts "sang of love, and not of fame; / Forgot was Britain's glory", which implies that the soldiers usually think about victory for Britain. Therefore, the soldiers must be fighting for Britain.

4.   A
'Rose' describes what the soldiers' song (or its tender passion) did, therefore it is a verb.

5.   a tear OR tears
Line 22 states that the song had a "tender passion", and line 25 states that the soldiers did not dare speak the name of their loved ones. This shows that the soldiers found the song emotional, and it is highly likely that the song caused them to cry.

6.   C
Lines 31-32 state "While the Crimean valleys learned / How English love remembers". This shows that the valleys in Crimea witnessed the soldiers' song, and for this to be the case, the battle must be taking place in Crimea.

7.   various answers possible
Line 37 states "Irish Nora's eyes are dim", and line 39 states "English Mary mourns for him", so you could have said that they are both 'sad', 'upset' or 'melancholy', for example.

8.   the soldiers who have died
Line 39 states "English Mary mourns for him", which means it is likely that some soldiers have died. Furthermore, line 41 states "still in honoured rest". Many people believe those who die whilst fighting for their country die with honour, and death is likely to be the only rest a soldier in battle receives.

9.   various answers possible
E.g. 'valour' means the same as 'bravery' or 'courage'.

Test 12 — pages 33-34

1.   E
'rising' is correct because it completes the phrase 'was rising', which is the correct form of the past continuous.

2.   C
'sank' is correct because it is the correct version of the verb in the past tense and remains consistent with the rest of the text.

3.   C
'nearer' is correct because it is the correct comparative form of 'near', and it describes the ship's movement.

4.   D
'could do' is correct because it uses the correct modal verb followed by the infinitive. Furthermore, it is a positive verb which means that a double negative is not created with the negative ('nothing') that follows.

5.   This lighthouse, famous for its multicoloured paintwork, is open to the public for the first time. At the heart of many dramatic rescues, it has a fascinating story to tell.
The bits that are underlined show where punctuation has been corrected. You get one mark for each of the following: a comma after 'lighthouse'; a comma after 'paintwork'; a full stop after 'time'; a capital letter at the start of 'At'; a comma after 'rescues'; and a full stop after 'tell'.

6.   A
'leept' should be 'leapt'.

7.   B
'retreived' should be 'retrieved' — the 'i' goes before the 'e'.

8.   B
'speciallity' should be 'speciality' — there is no need to double the 'l' before adding the suffix 'ity'.

9.   C
'inhabitents' should be 'inhabitants' — the ending is 'ants'.

10.   D
'absense' should be 'absence' — the ending is 'ce'.

11.   D
'dissappeared' should be 'disappeared' — the prefix is 'dis', which is added to the root word 'appeared', therefore the word should have only one 's'.

12.   N
There are no mistakes in this line.

13.   C
'unaturally' should be 'unnaturally' — the prefix 'un' is added to 'naturally', so 'n' appears twice in the word.

Puzzles 4 — page 35

Treasure Trail

a) Start at the blue <u>manner</u> house. — **manor**
b) Walk <u>rite</u> briskly for seven squares. — **right**
c) <u>Sale</u> north across stormy seas for four squares. — **Sail**
d) Go west through the <u>heard</u> of cows, and carry on for four squares. — **herd**
e) Travel south over <u>baron</u> land until you reach the lake. — **barren**

You should have collected **5** coins along the way.

Country Confusion

Scotland   Pakistan   Portugal
Hidden country: *Russia*

Test 13 — pages 36-38

1.   various answers possible
You get one mark for either of these explanations: they are more like acquaintances than friends — lines 3-4 state "Something that for lack of any other name might be called friendship existed and always had existed between Marilla Cuthbert and Mrs Rachel", which shows that their relationship is only described as a friendship because there isn't another suitable word; OR they have an unlikely friendship because they are so different (lines 5 mentions their "dissimilarity").

2.   various answers possible
E.g. 'dissimilarity' means the same as 'difference' or 'variance'.

3.   various answers possible
E.g. Marilla's "narrow experience" suggests she is naive and unworldly. Her "rigid conscience" suggests she is virtuous and moral.

4.   A
Lines 9-10 state "there was a saving something about her mouth".

5.   C
Lines 15-17 state "she had known that the sight of Matthew jaunting off so unaccountably would be too much for her neighbor's curiosity".

6.   jaunting
"Jaunting" describes what Matthew was doing.

7.   to collect an orphan
Lines 19-20 state "We're getting a little boy from an orphan asylum in Nova Scotia and he's coming on the train tonight".

8.   C
'Astonished' is another way of saying 'shocked' or 'astounded'.

9.   B
Rachel is so astonished by the news that even though Marilla is not the type of person to joke, Rachel has no choice but to consider the possibility that she is joking.

Test 14 — pages 39-40

1. **Keeping hens is a rewarding hobb<u>y</u>, especially if you rescue them from a battery farm, because you'll have the satisfac<u>ti</u>on of knowing you've given an animal the opp<u>o</u>rtunity of a better exist<u>e</u>nce.**

The bits that are underlined show where a spelling mistake has been corrected. You get one mark for each of the following words you have spelt correctly: 'hobby', 'satisfaction', 'opportunity', 'existence'.

2. **<u>"</u>Great<u>!"</u> shouted Jeff<u>,</u> glaring upwards as the traffic lights turned to red<u>.</u> <u>H</u>e'd been late yesterday as well, so he couldn't believe it was happening again.**

The bits that are underlined show where punctuation has been corrected. You get one mark for each of the following: speech marks before "Great"; an exclamation mark (OR a comma) after "Great"; speech marks after "Great!"; a comma after "Jeff"; a full stop after "red"; and a capital letter at the start of "he".

3. **C**
'in' is correct because it describes where Jo paused.

4. **B**
'could' makes the most sense in this sentence.

5. **D**
'long' is correct because it describes how far Jo has left to swim.

6. **D**
'was' is correct because it is in the correct tense and it agrees with the subject 'she'.

7. **A**
'if' is correct because it introduces the possibility that she may or may not reach the island.

8. **B**
'past' is correct because it is an adverb that describes where the competitors are swimming — all the other options are verbs.

9. **E**
'had' is correct because it is in the correct tense and it agrees with the subject 'she'.

10. **C**
'began' is correct because it is in the correct tense.

Test 15 — pages 41-43

1. **C**
Lines 2-4 state "The large standing stones arranged in rings that form Stonehenge provide a unique insight into prehistoric times. For this reason, many have fought for its protection".

2. **various answers possible**
E.g. The stones provide us with an unusual opportunity to learn something about prehistoric times.

3. **There are no written records from this time.**
This is stated in line 7.

4. **B**
Lines 11-13 state "Historians and visitors alike are amazed that people with such limited technology managed to transport and arrange the stones in this way".

5. **various answers possible**
E.g. Line 10 states that bluestones are found at Stonehenge, and line 15 states "bluestones were thought to have curative powers". 'Curative' means 'healing'.

6. **speculation**
This word appears in line 17.

7. **B**
Lines 10-11 state that the bluestones were quarried in Wales, but it does not mention where the sarsen stones came from.

8. **C**
'Among' is a preposition because it describes where visitors were allowed to walk.

9. **C**
'Peaceful' and 'undisturbed' are adjectives because they describe the historical site.

Puzzles 5 — page 44

Verbsearch

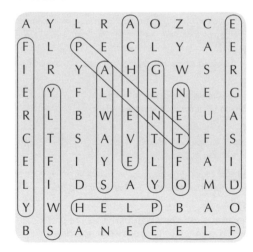

Verbs: *achieve, disagree, flee, help, paint*
Adverbs: *always, fiercely, gently, often, swiftly*

Balloon Bedlam

Adjective: *healthy, wise*
Pronoun: *they, you*
Preposition: *onto, among*
Conjunction: *and, or*
Noun: *greed, wealth*

Test 16 — pages 45-46

1. C
'more' introduces a comparison, so completes the phrase 'more...than'.

2. B
'being' is correct because it is the progressive form of 'to be'.

3. A
'could' makes the most sense in this sentence as it is a modal verb that introduces the possibilities of what he could do on his days off.

4. E
'every' is correct because it completes the phrase 'every day' which makes the most sense in this sentence.

5. Dawn was having trouble dec<u>id</u>ing <u>which</u> new car to pur<u>ch</u>ase. She wanted something ec<u>o</u>nomical, but because she was on a very tight bud<u>ge</u>t, her options were qui<u>te</u> limited.

The bits that are underlined show where a spelling mistake has been corrected. You get one mark for each of the following words you have spelt correctly: 'deciding', 'which', 'purchase', 'economical', 'budget', 'quite'.

6. C
'holiday's' is incorrect — it is a plural so it doesn't need an apostrophe.

7. A
'Mr Smiths' is incorrect — there should be an apostrophe before the final 's' to indicate possession.

8. A
'six week' is incorrect — it should be 'six-week'. 'six-week' is modifying 'break' so it needs a hyphen to avoid making its meaning ambiguous.

9. A
There should be a comma after 'holiday' to separate the two clauses.

10. N
There are no errors in this line.

11. B
There should be a full stop after 'work' to mark the end of the sentence.

12. N
There are no errors in this line.

13. A
There should be a set of speech marks after the exclamation mark.

Test 17 — pages 47-49

1. various answers possible
You get one mark for either of the following explanations: Ellie's walk had a purpose rather than just being for fun (lines 3-4 state "today's walk was filled with purpose: she needed to catch an animal on camera for a wildlife project at school"); OR she walked along a path that she had never taken before (line 7 describes "a path she had never seen before").

2. D
Lines 4-6 state "Ellie felt a shiver engulf her as the path took her through the copse, and the sun gave way to the leafy canopy". The path she was following went into the shade of the trees, making her feel cold.

3. C
Lines 8-9 state "seized by curiosity, Ellie decided to follow it".

4. B
Ellie comes across "a small body of water" at the top of the hill, and this is where she sees the creature.

5. C
'Obscured' has a similar meaning to 'concealed' or 'hidden'.

6. C
'She' carries out the actions 'arrived' and 'shouted', so 'she' is the subject.

7. various answers possible
E.g. 'oscillating' means the same as 'fluctuating' or 'changing'.

8. D
Lines 19-20 state "her feelings of excitement rapidly turned to shock when she saw the picture she had just taken". 'Astounded' is another way of saying 'shocked'.

9. "smooth silky surface"
This phrase on line 21 is an example of alliteration because it contains three consecutive words beginning with the same sound — 's'.

Test 18 — pages 50-51

1. B
'rode' is correct because it is the past tense form of 'ride'.

2. C
'was' is correct because it agrees with the singular noun 'field' and is in the past tense.

3. D
'their' is correct — it indicates possession of the dog.

4. E
'where' is correct — it refers to the location.

5. **To make Yorkshire puddings, mix flour, eggs and milk in a bowl. Heat some oil in the Yorkshire pudding t<u>ins,</u> then add the mixture to the tins, dividing it equally between them. <u>C</u>ook for 20 minutes.**

The bits that are underlined show where punctuation has been corrected. You get one mark for each of the following: a comma after 'puddings'; a comma after 'flour'; a full stop after 'bowl'; writing 'tins' instead of 'tin's'; a comma after 'tins'; and a capital letter at the start of 'Cook'.

6. **A**
'warilly' should be spelt 'warily' — the suffix 'ly' is added to the adjective 'wary', and the final 'y' in 'wary' changes to an 'i'.

7. **C**
'huried' should be spelt 'hurried' — the root word is 'hurry', so this word should be spelt with a double 'r'.

8. **B**
'entranse' should be spelt 'entrance' — the ending is 'ance'.

9. **B**
'lengthend' should be spelt 'lengthened' — the suffix 'ed' is added to 'lengthen'.

10. **A**
'eventualy' should be spelt 'eventually' — the suffix 'ly' is added to the root word 'eventual', so it needs two 'l's.

11. **D**
'faigning' should be spelt 'feigning'.

12. **A**
'confidance' should be 'confidence' — the ending is 'ence'.

13. **N**
There are no spelling mistakes in this line.

Puzzles 6 — page 52

Place the Word Types

The *fluffy* cat *and* the friendly *poodle played carefully* with the mouse *in* the garden.
The new word spelt by the shaded letters is *fallen*.

Word Type Scramble

HASTILY — *adverb*
DEPART — *verb*
ABOVE — *preposition*
FURIOUS — *adjective*

Test 19 — pages 53-55

1. **various answers possible**
You get one mark for either of the following: "I wandered lonely as a cloud" (line 1); OR "Continuous as the stars that shine" (line 7). Both of these use 'as' to compare two things, therefore they are similes.

2. **B**
The daffodils are said to be "Beside the lake" (line 5), "beneath the trees" (line 5) and "Along the margin of a bay" (line 10), but not on the hills.

3. **D**
The daffodils are "dancing", which is a human action, so this must be an example of personification.

4. **B**
The daffodils are described as "Continuous as the stars", meaning they appear to stretch as far as the stars.

5. **A**
Lines 13-14 state "The waves beside them danced; but they / Out-did the sparkling waves in glee", meaning the daffodils are more joyful than the waves.

6. **preposition**
'Beside' specifies where the waves danced, so it is a preposition.

7. **The poet had been looking at the daffodils for a long time but didn't realise at the time how happy they made him.**
'wealth' is another word for 'value', so these lines mean that the poet was unaware of the value of the daffodils, or how happy they were making him until much later.

8. **He brings the sight of the daffodils back to memory.**
The 'inward eye' refers to the poet's imagination.

9. **B**
'Solitude' is closest in meaning to 'isolation'.

Test 20 — pages 56-58

1. **various answers possible**
E.g. The average human is a much slower runner than the average horse, so it was daring to suggest that a human could outrun a horse.

2. **to attract people to the town centre to boost the local tourist economy**
The race was introduced in an attempt to improve the local tourist economy, so starting the race in the town centre might have helped to attract people there.

3. **various answers possible**
E.g. In this passage, 'take the helm' means 'take charge of the situation' or 'oversee the planning' of the event.

4. **B**
The first race was held in 1980, and line 12 states "the course was altered two years later".

5. **A**
Lines 17-18 state that "humans tend to have superior endurance", meaning they can exercise for longer periods.

6. **various answers possible**
E.g. 'susceptible' means the same as 'prone' or 'inclined'.

7. **C**
'They' refers to 'the horses', so it is a pronoun.

8. **Hot weather gives humans an advantage in the race as horses tend to overheat and therefore suffer on hot days.**

Lines 18-19 state "Horses are also susceptible to overheating".

9. **various answers possible**

You get one mark for either of the following explanations: although he won the race, he is an elite marathon runner, meaning he is faster than the average marathon runner; OR he was the first man in 25 years to win the race, meaning human victory in the race is rare.

Test 21 — pages 59-60

1. **"This steak is marv<u>e</u>llous," Frances said to George, in their favourite Ital<u>i</u>an restaurant. "Is your chicken nice?" she asked. George nodded enthusiasticall<u>y</u>, <u>u</u>nable to speak through a mouthf<u>u</u>l of food.**

The bits that are underlined show where a spelling mistake has been corrected. You get one mark for each of the following words you have spelt correctly: 'marvellous', 'Italian', 'enthusiastically', 'unable' and 'mouthful'.

2. **"It<u>'</u>s so busy!<u>"</u> yelled Natalie<u>,</u> Tariq and Rosie simultaneously, staring through the shop<u>'</u>s window<u>.</u> Everyone was desperate to take advantage of the half-price sale.**

The bits that are underlined show where punctuation has been corrected. You get one mark for each of the following: an apostrophe in 'It's'; quotation marks after the exclamation mark; a comma after 'Natalie'; an apostrophe in 'shop's'; and a full stop after 'window'.

3. **D**

'was' is correct — it agrees with the singular noun 'house' and is in the past tense.

4. **C**

'couldn't' makes the most sense in this sentence.

5. **A**

'over' is the adverb that best describes where Kieran wandered.

6. **D**

'knew' is correct — it is the past tense form of 'know'.

7. **D**

'its' is correct — it refers to the house's possession of the door.

8. **C**

'except' completes the phrase 'except for'.

9. **A**

'further' makes the most sense in this sentence — it is the correct comparative form of 'far'.

10. **B**

'heard' is correct — it is the past tense form of 'hear'.

Puzzles 7 — page 61

Spelling Secrets

This morning, I went for an ***extremely*** long walk. I went ***through*** the fields and towards the ***forest***. Then when I got home, I ***perused*** my favourite book.

There are four mistakes, so the meeting is at ***4*** o'clock.

Literary Link-up

The water was a handful of crystals as it smashed over the rocks. — ***metaphor***

The water was chattering and gurgling over the pebbles. — ***personification***

The water was whirling and wheeling down the waterfall. — ***alliteration***

The water was as clear as a polished crystal. — ***simile***

Test 22 — pages 62-63

1. **C**

'should have' makes the most sense in this sentence as it indicates something that should have been done.

2. **D**

'thought' makes the most sense in this sentence — it's the past tense of 'think'.

3. **B**

'before' is the only word that makes sense in this sentence.

4. **D**

'which' is correct because it refers back to the leaves and bits of tree.

5. **Our babysitter is a complet<u>e</u> bore. She sits idly on the sofa the <u>w</u>hole time, and makes us endure te<u>di</u>ous television program<u>m</u>es instead of entertaining us. She's so mis<u>e</u>rable that it's a reli<u>ef</u> when she leaves.**

The bits that are underlined show where a spelling mistake has been corrected. You get one mark for each of the following words you have spelt correctly: 'complete', 'whole', 'tedious', 'programmes', 'miserable' and 'relief'.

6. **D**

There should be a comma after 'Tuesdays' to separate the items in the list.

7. **C**

'were' should be 'we're' — there needs to be an apostrophe before the 'r' because 'we're' is a contraction of 'we are'.

8. **C**

There should be a bracket after 'Speaksworth' to enclose the extra information — brackets are always used in pairs.

9. **C**

There should be a comma after the word 'strings' to separate the items in the list.

10.   D
There shouldn't be a comma before the word 'we' —
it's part of the same clause so it isn't necessary.

11.   N
There are no mistakes in this line.

12.   A
There should be a single quotation mark after the
word 'Song' to enclose the title of the piece.

13.   C
There should be a capital letter at the start of 'it'll'
because this is the first word that is spoken.

Test 23 — pages 64-66

1.   various answers possible
E.g. 'fleeting' means the same as 'quick' or 'brief'.

2.   A
Line 3 describes the house as "crumbling", implying it is
damaged. 'Decrepit' has a similar meaning to 'damaged'.

3.   various answers possible
You get one mark for either of these explanations:
Lowri is now at a higher position than she was before,
giving her a better view than at first (lines 1-2
state "Until they crested the ridge, where the view
of it was clearer than it had been from the road");
OR the road she was on was winding east and west,
causing the farmhouse to disappear from view (lines
5-6 describe her "fleeting glimpses of a building as
the road snaked eastwards and westwards").

4.   C
A simile compares one thing to something
else. Lowri is comparing the farmhouse to a
familiar face, so this must be a simile.

5.   B
Lines 9-10 show that Lowri's colleague offered three
excuses why Lowri shouldn't approach the farmhouse.

6.   The wall is no longer intact.
Lines 11-12 state "The metal front gate
still stood intact, though most of the wall on
either side had not been so fortunate".

7.   C
Lines 14-15 state "A shaft of sunlight shone through
the window at the far end", therefore it must be false
that it is already dark when they find the farmhouse.

**8.   Mrs Josephine insisted that her house
was kept clean.**
A stickler is someone who insists on something.

9.   various answers possible
E.g. Lowri is sad that the farmhouse is no
longer like it used to be. Line 15 states it is
"A pity" that the house is no longer clean.

Test 24 — pages 67-68

1.   C
'are' is correct because it is the correct
tense and the verb agrees with the plural
subject — 'my aunts and uncles'.

2.   E
'they're' is correct because the pronoun
('they') refers back to 'siblings', and the verb
('are') agrees with the plural pronoun.

3.   D
'be' makes the most sense in this sentence
— it completes the infinitive form 'to be'.

4.   D
'whoever' makes the most sense in this
sentence because it is not referring to a
specific person, but to one of many people.

**5.   The three puppies — Ronald, Nancy and
Spot — have just arrived at the pet shop
(the one behind the park).**
The bits that are underlined show where punctuation
has been corrected. You get one mark for each
of the following: a comma after 'Ronald'; a capital
letter at the start of 'Nancy'; a capital letter at the
start of 'Spot'; a dash before 'have'; a bracket before
'the'; and a full stop after the closing bracket.

6.   D
'beneeth' should be spelt 'beneath'.

7.   D
'devise' should be 'device' — 'devise' is a
verb, whereas 'device' is a noun.

8.   C
'acess' should be 'access' — the
word is spelt with two 'c's.

9.   D
'organisatian' should be 'organisation'
— the ending is 'tion'.

10.   C
'neccessary' should be 'necessary' — 'c'
only appears once in the word.

11.   A
'gracefuly' should be 'gracefully' — the
suffix 'ly' is added to 'graceful'.

12.   C
'aprehended' should be 'apprehended' —
the word is spelt with a double 'p'.

13.   N
There are no mistakes in this line.

Puzzles 8 — page 69

Stepping Stones

HAPPY *ELATED JOYFUL DELIGHTED JOLLY MERRY*

Word Chain

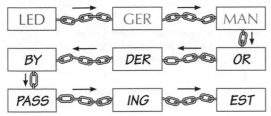

LED → GER → MAN

BY ← DER ← OR

PASS → ING → EST

Test 25 — pages 70-72

1. various answers possible
E.g. Lines 1-2 state that the island is "far removed from the hustle and bustle of the mainland", meaning the island is much quieter and more peaceful than the mainland.

2. various answers possible
E.g. 'submerged' has a similar meaning to 'immersed' or 'covered in water'.

3. various answers possible
E.g. Line 4 states that the route to the island is "submerged as the sea rolls in", meaning that tourists could become stranded if they travel during high tide because the path connecting the mainland to the island becomes cut off. If tourists check the tide patterns, they can plan to travel during low tide.

4. C
Lines 6-7 state that "the tidal refuge hut is available in times of need", meaning tourists can escape the high tide there if necessary.

5. various answers possible
E.g. "a commanding position" presents the castle as a prominent and an important part of the island.

6. B
'Turbulent' has a similar meaning to 'chaotic' or 'unstable'.

7. by fishing
Line 15 states that Northeasterners "made a living from catching herrings" — herrings are a type of fish.

8. C
'Autumn' and 'winter' are both abstract nouns — they are names of seasons, which are not concrete objects.

9. various answers possible.
E.g. Lines 16-19 suggest that the harbour suffers the effects of unpredictable weather. 'Temperamental' is another word for 'unpredictable'.

Test 26 — pages 73-74

1. C
'served' makes the most sense in this sentence — it is the past participle of 'serve'.

2. A
'a' is the determiner that makes the most sense in this sentence because it agrees with the singular noun 'meal' and is correct before the initial 'r' sound.

3. B
'of' makes the most sense in this sentence as it completes the phrase 'a mixture of'.

4. D
'There's' is correct as it is a contraction of 'There is' and 'is' agrees with the singular 'one ingredient' that follows.

5. C
'which' is correct because it introduces the relative clause that follows.

6. E
'turns' is correct as it agrees with the singular subject 'saffron' and is in the present tense like the rest of the text.

7. A
'Traditionally' is correct because it is an adverb that describes how paella is cooked.

8. B
'is cooked' makes the most sense in this sentence — it is the present passive form of 'to cook'.

9. Contrary to popular belief, a goldfish's memory spans beyond three seconds, and scientists believe they can recall information for up to five months, so the general consensus is that fish aren't that forgetful after all.
The bits that are underlined show where a spelling mistake has been corrected. You get one mark for each of the following words you have spelt correctly: 'Contrary', 'scientists', 'information', 'consensus', 'forgetful'.

10. During the second round, the first dancing duo — Tom and June — will perform the tango. This will be the twenty-first time that they've danced together.
The bits that are underlined show where punctuation has been corrected. You get one mark for each of the following: a comma after 'round'; a dash after 'duo'; a capital letter at the start of 'Tom'; a full stop after 'tango'; and a hyphen in 'twenty-first'.

Test 27 — pages 75-77

1. The narrator is in his bedroom.
Lines 3-4 state "suddenly there came a tapping, / As of someone gently rapping, rapping at my chamber door". 'Chamber' is another word for 'bedroom'.

2.   "each separate dying ember"
In line 8, the embers of the fire are described as "dying", meaning that they will not give out heat for much longer.

3.   C
Lines 9-10 state "vainly I had sought to borrow / From my books surcease of sorrow". "surcease of sorrow" means "relief from feeling sad", so reading books helps the narrator stop himself from feeling sad.

4.   It scares the narrator.
Line 14 states that the narrator is filled with "fantastic terrors never felt before".

5.   various answers possible
E.g. He tells himself that the noise is caused by a visitor — lines 17-18 state "Some late visitor entreating entrance at my chamber door;— / This it is and nothing more".

6.   A
'Longer' is an adverb as it is used to describe the verb 'hesitating'.

7.   various answers possible
E.g. 'implore' means the same as 'plead' or 'beg'.

8.   C
"tapping, tapping" is an example of onomatopoeia — 'tap' sounds like the noise it describes.

9.   various answers possible
E.g. Lines 23-24 state "here I opened wide the door;— / Darkness there, and nothing more" which shows that there isn't a visitor at the door.

Puzzles 9 — page 78

Word Family Frolics

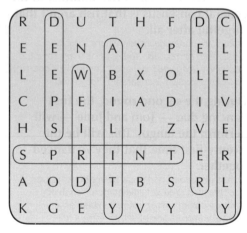

Double Trouble

a) *desserts* (makes '*stressed*' backwards)
b) *live* (makes '*evil*' backwards)
c) *star* (makes '*rats*' backwards)

Test 28 — pages 79-80

1.   N
There are no mistakes in this line.

2.   C
There should be a comma after the word 'sister' to separate the extra information from the rest of the sentence.

3.   C
There should be a punctuation mark (either a comma or an exclamation mark) after the word 'space' to end the speech.

4.   C
'its' should be 'it's' — there needs to be an apostrophe before the 's' to show that 'it's' is a contraction of 'it is'.

5.   A
There should be a capital letter at the start of 'mum' because this is a proper noun.

6.   D
There should be a semi-colon after the closing bracket to separate the items in the list.

7.   B
The semi-colon should come after the word 'shop' and not after 'and'.

8.   N
There are no mistakes in this line.

9.   C
'with' is correct because it completes the phrase 'an obsession with'.

10.   D
'his' is correct because it is a possessive adjective that refers to Liam's possession of the bedroom.

11.   C
'Despite' is correct because it completes the phrase 'despite this'.

12.   D
'spacious' makes the most sense in this sentence because it forms the comparative adjective 'more spacious'. (Adjectives that only have one syllable like 'big' or 'large' gain the suffix 'er' to form their comparative adjective.)

13.   We're doing a class art project in mixed media. Our teacher says we all have to make a contribution, whether we choose paint, collage or sculpture. We've split it into eight separate sections, so there's lots of variety.
The bits that are underlined show where a spelling mistake has been corrected. You get one mark for each of the following words you have spelt correctly: 'project', 'contribution', 'whether', 'collage', 'separate' and 'there's'.

Test 29 — pages 81-82

1.   B
'beat' makes the most sense in this sentence — it is the imperative form of the verb which is common in recipes.

2.   E
'until' is correct because it tells the reader how long to beat the sugar and butter for.

3.   A
'taking' makes the most sense in this sentence — it forms part of the adverbial that gives more specific information about adding the two eggs.

4.   D
'a' is the correct article to go before 'spoon' in this context.

5.   We're going to Raj's birthday party tomorrow which includes rugby, tag, a birthday tea, a film and a sleepover.
The bits that are underlined show where punctuation has been corrected. You get one mark for each of the following: a capital letter at the start of 'were'; an apostrophe in 'we're'; an apostrophe in 'Raj's'; a comma after 'tag'; a comma after 'tea'; and a full stop after 'sleepover'.

6.   C
'nateive' should be 'native' — the 'e' is not necessary.

7.   D
'elsewear' should be 'elsewhere' — 'where' is the correct ending because it refers to a location.

8.   A
'pray' should be 'prey' — 'pray' means 'to communicate with God or another deity', whereas 'prey' means 'an animal hunted by another animal for food'.

9.   C
'triggerred' should be 'triggered' — the suffix 'ed' is added to the root word 'trigger', so the word only needs one 'r' before the suffix.

10.   C
'destributed' should be 'distributed' — the root word is 'distribute'.

11.   N
There are no mistakes in this line.

12.   C
'preperation' should be 'preparation' — the root word is 'prepare'.

13.   B
'protien' should be 'protein' — this is an exception to the 'i before e' rule.

Test 30 — pages 83-85

1.   He was inspired by watching embers rising up a chimney.
Lines 2-3 state "witnessing the sparks being lifted by a force gave him an idea".

2.   D
Lines 6-7 state "the lighter, hot air could lift objects through the colder, surrounding air".

3.   C
'Captivated' means 'enthralled' or 'fascinated'. Joseph refers to his discovery as "astonishing" (line 8), which reveals his enthusiasm.

4.   B
Lines 13-14 state "This new balloon surpassed that, flying for twenty-five minutes".

5.   Many people do not believe that the story about the pilots offering the farmers champagne is true.
'Legend' refers to something that is said to have happened, but has not been proven to be true.

6.   adverb
'Suddenly' is describing the verb 'became'.

7.   They used hydrogen instead of hot air.
Lines 18-19 state "Designers started using hydrogen — a lighter gas — instead of hot air".

8.   B
Lines 12-13 state that the "first flight to carry live passengers had taken place on 19th September the same year", so the first flight was not in November.

9.   A
'Circumnavigate' means 'to go around something'.

Puzzles 10 — page 86

Repair It

*tele*p*ort* *system* *relation* *dreaming* *balance*
Answer to the joke: **Aye matey!**

Cube Words

dance place candle laces
Nine letter word: *landscape*

Test 31 — pages 87-88

1.   It was a gloo<u>my</u> day; the wind was bluste<u>r</u>ing loudly against the windows. The rain fell <u>r</u>elentlessly thro<u>ugh</u>out the day, so many at<u>t</u>empted to protect them<u>se</u>lves with spindly umbrellas.
The bits that are underlined show where a spelling mistake has been corrected. You get one mark for each of the following words you have spelt correctly: 'gloomy', 'blustering', 'relentlessly', 'throughout', 'attempted', 'themselves'.

2. "What a day!" sighed Sarah, throwing her bag onto the living room armchair. She collapsed, exhausted, onto the couch, closing her eyes immediately.

The bits that are underlined show where punctuation has been corrected. You get one mark for each of the following: a speech mark after the exclamation mark; a comma after 'Sarah'; a capital letter at the start of 'She'; and a comma after 'exhausted'.

3.   B
'going' completes the phrase 'I am going camping' — it is the present continuous form of 'to go' in the first person singular.

4.   C
'have to' makes the most sense in this sentence.

5.   D
'will' is correct as it is referring to the possibility of being able to go out for walks at a point in the future.

6.   E
'have' is correct because it completes the phrase 'have picnics'.

7.   A
'rained' is correct because it is used in connection with the conditional tense 'I wouldn't mind', so it is expressing the possibility of what may or may not happen if it rained.

8.   D
'if' makes the most sense in this sentence as it is referring to the possibility that it will rain.

9.   A
'you're' is correct as it is a contraction of 'you are'.

10.   C
'having' completes the phrase 'having fun'.

Test 32 — pages 89-91

1.   various answers possible
E.g. 'beat' means the same as 'tired' or 'exhausted'.

2.   horse and carriage driver
Lines 1-2 make reference to "a shabby, miserable-looking driver, who went by the name of 'Seedy Sam'" and line 8 mentions "the use of a cab and two horses".

3.   D
Line 3 states ""You and your horse look more fit for the police station", suggesting Seedy Sam looks 'disreputable' or 'dishonourable'.

4.   The fares are fixed at a low price.
Line 7 states "the fares that are fixed so low".

5.   C
Lines 7-9 state "a man has to pay eighteen shillings a day for the use of a cab and two horses, as many of us have to do in the season, and must make that up before we earn a penny for ourselves".

6.   D
'True' is an adjective — it is describing 'that'. 'That' is referring to a previous statement, which is treated like a noun in this context.

7.   five
Lines 12-13 state "I've six of 'em, and only one earns anything".

8.   D
On line 8, Seedy Sam complains that it's expensive to rent horses and carriages, and also says "with so many to feed" (line 16), suggesting he has a large family. He does not mention a lack of customers though.

9.   B
Lines 14-15 state "Skinner never gives a day if he can help it", suggesting he is 'unforgiving' or 'unsympathetic'.

Test 33 — pages 92-94

1.   "forming giant curtains"
Lines 3-4 say that the lights are a giant curtain. Since they're not actually a giant curtain, this must be a metaphor.

2.   D
'Eventually' is an adverb as it describes the verb 'grow'.

3.   various answers possible
E.g. 'phenomenon' means the same as 'rare sight' or 'rare occurrence'.

4.   C
Lines 7-8 state that the natural light show "occurs above the North Pole".

5.   D
'Notoriously' has a similar meaning to 'infamously' or 'widely known'.

6.   C
Line 10 states "precise sightings are notoriously difficult to predict" — sightings of them are rare because they are likely to only occur by chance.

7.   They can cause power blackouts, leaving people without electricity.
Lines 11-12 state "these light shows have been known to cause power blackouts", meaning the Northern Lights can cause electricity power cuts.

8.   B
Lines 13-14 state "note that they aren't visible to the naked eye during the day".

9.   various answers possible
E.g. 'one of the most sought-after sights' means 'one of the most wanted/desirable things to see'.